THE KNIGHTS
OF THE GOLDEN TABLE

THE
KNIGHTS OF
THE GOLDEN TABLE

E. M. ALMEDINGEN

WITH DRAWINGS
BY CHARLES KEEPING

J. B. LIPPINCOTT COMPANY

PHILADELPHIA   1964   NEW YORK

TO
F. M. PILKINGTON
WITH LOVE
AND
DEEP GRATITUDE

Contents

Foreword

THE twelve stories in this book are taken from what is known as the Kiev Cycle, a vast collection of songs and ballads, their origin nearly one thousand years old. In those days there was no Russia as we know it today. There were just three principalities, Kiev on the river Dnieper, Novgorod to the north on the river Volkh, and Pskov a little to the west. They were founded in or about A.D. 862 by three Vikings of the tribe of Rus in Scandinavia. The first chronicler of Russia, Nestor, writing some three centuries later, said that the three Vikings had been invited to come by the scattered Slav tribes then inhabiting the country. "Our land is vast and plentiful, but there is no order in it. Come and rule over us."

It was Rurik the Viking who founded Kiev, and the Prince Vladimir in this book was his direct descendant. Vladimir's mother was Helga (Olga in Russian), a wise and beautiful princess, the first in the country to become a Christian. About A.D. 988 Vladimir decided to marry, and he chose Anna, sister of the Greek Emperors, Basil and Constantine, who refused their consent to the marriage unless Vladimir became a Christian. He agreed, and soon afterward he had all his people baptized in the river Dnieper.

Even during his lifetime Vladimir was something of a legendary figure. They said of him that he swam like a fish, fought like a lion, and sang like a nightingale. He was

9

also as cruel as a tiger, but he had concern for his people and great pride in his dominions. He had inherited Kiev as a well-fortified keep standing on a hill high above the Dnieper. He made it so beautiful that travelers never tired of singing its praises. It had a big cathedral, St. Sophia's, and four hundred churches, a huge market place, and wide streets fronted by exquisitely built houses of well-seasoned and richly carved timber. Churches and city walls alone were built of stone. Vladimir spared neither money nor energy to make Kiev preeminent among other cities. He invited architects, craftsmen and scholars to his court, encouraged learning and trade, and himself dispensed justice. The humblest among his subjects had the right to see the Prince in his hall.

Kiev had its Parliament, known as *vieche*, and all important matters were decided by Vladimir together with his people. A great bell would summon them to St. Sophia's square, and every ten houses in the city had their elected spokesman, whose counsel was always listened to by the Prince.

Yet Vladimir's reign was far from peaceful. His principality was in constant peril of invasion. Southward lay the vast as yet unconquered lands peopled by the wild nomadic Slav tribes—Polovtzy, Pechenegy and others, and Vladimir had to fight them all. He had a fine enough army, and he also had a very special "Fellowship," known as his *Druzhina* (from *Drug* which means friend in Russian). They rode nearest to the Prince in battle and had the right to a share of wine from his gold cup at all banquets in the hall of the palace.

Kiev early became famous for its armorers. Vladimir's Knights wore hauberks, or tunics, of finely meshed mail;

their helmets, conical in shape, had no visors, nor did they wear greaves. They rode in white linen breeches. For arms they carried short swords, pikes, axes and sometimes cudgels tipped with iron. Valor and honesty were the two essentials necessary for election to the *Druzhina*. Rank and birth went for nothing. There were peasants' sons, priests' sons and artisans' sons among the Knights. At banquets they sat at a long table made of oak and plated all over with gold.

Vladimir's palace was thrown open to all his people. When not away from Kiev, he loved giving great feasts. Baked sturgeon and pike, roast swans and geese, enormous meat pies, porridge spiced with poppy seeds, and gingerbread were served at the table. They drank mead, a very potent concoction made of honey, and wine imported from Greece and Italy. For entertainment the Prince offered music, singing and dancing. His court musicians played on string instruments somewhat resembling ancient psalteries, and they composed songs in honor of Vladimir's brave Knights. All those songs began and ended with a few lines of praise to Vladimir, "the little red sun of Kiev."

There they sat at the golden table, the Prince and his gallant Fellowship, all in fine white shirts and loose coats of scarlet or blue, great gold buckles gleaming with jewels on their right shoulders, their long hair and beards carefully combed for the feast, their feet comfortable in boots of soft green leather. Yet down in the well of the great hall their armor, swords and pikes lay on the mosaic floor. Outside, in the vast courtyard, stablemen had the Knights' horses in readiness, because even during peaceful spells they had to be on the alert in case the watchman's urgent trumpet were to announce the approach of an enemy.

Vladimir died full of years and glory, and so did his valiant *Druzhina*, but the stories of their exploits went on being sung from one generation to another, and it was fitting for the nation to remember those fearless men who put duty and honor before all else, who fought like lions and never surrendered, and died in the manner of heroes "for the little red sun Vladimir and for Holy Kiev."

It was inevitable for those songs, which were never written down but either sung or recited, to move away, however gradually, from a strict historical pattern. In the centuries that followed, the very names of the savage Slav tribes which had so harassed Kiev in Vladimir's day were forgotten by the majority of the people, yet the memory of a far deadlier enemy was graven in their consciousness: the Tartars.

The Tartars did not invade Russia until well into the middle of the thirteenth century, more than two hundred years after Vladimir's death. It was in 1241 that Kiev was sacked by them, and not until 1380 was Tartar strength shaken by the Russian victory at Kulikovo. The Tartar yoke, however, was not ended at Kulikovo. It continued for another century or so until Ivan III, Prince of Moscow, refused to pay any more tribute to the Great Khan.

Thus, historically, there were no Tartars in the Kiev of Vladimir, but that did not matter to the creators of the Russian epos. The terrible might of the Tartar was—as they thought—alone fit to be matched against the valor of Vladimir's Knights. Thus it happens that it is the Tartar who figures as the archenemy in these stories.

The imagination of the race, however, did not stop there. The stature of Vladimir's Knights grew and grew with each passing generation. Gradually shapes and images born of a blending of pure fantasy with the pagan past entered upon the scene. Witches and warlocks had always been there, but even they did not suffice. Dragons and serpents came in, horses and birds were made to speak in human language, and inanimate objects came to be endowed with magical powers. Knights were said to fight with magic swords and cudgels, they loosed arrows "tipped with the flame from heaven," they were given magical protection from danger, and their horses flew on wings. The very weapons they carried were no ordinary ones: Ilya's marvellous cudgel is one such instance out of many.

Yet, all such embellishments and exaggerations notwithstanding, the heart of the great story remained unchanged down the centuries: the valor of the Knights, their integrity, their devotion to the Prince and the country, their horror at the very idea of dishonor—all these remained.

The theme inspired many Russian musicians, painters, and poets, and just about one hundred years ago a few scholarly men, determined not to let such a great heritage perish from the national memory, began traveling up and down Russia. They listened to the peasants singing and reciting, and they committed the epics to writing. Presently they were published. In Russian, they are called *byliny*, a word originating from *byl* which means "a true story." It might well be rendered as "it so happened."

The present collection is but a fragment of that vast epos. The cycle of Ilya alone runs into more than one hundred songs, most of which have more than one variant. Nobody knows the exact number of the *Druzhina*, but it is unlikely that they were fewer than a hundred. There may well have been more of them. Here, just twelve of them make their appearance, the twelve whose exploits have left the deepest impression on the national folklore.

Finally, it might not be out of place to mention one point of affinity between Vladimir's *Druzhina* and King Arthur's Knights of the Round Table. It is true that Vladimir's dedicated Fellowship never went in search of the Holy Grail. None the less, there is a bridge between Tintagel and Kiev: the unquenchable thirst to see Good triumph over Evil.

E. M. Almedingen.

How Three Pilgrims Called Ilya to the Rescue of Kiev

How Three Pilgrims Called Ilya to the Rescue of Kiev

PRINCE VLADIMIR's reign was still at its beginning when things began to go badly for him. All the men he could muster were busy to the south and the east of the city, warding off the onslaught of the Tartars. To keep so many men under arms cost much money. Kiev was wealthy enough, but its prosperity always depended on trade, and a terrible brigand, called Solovey, saw an opportunity to enrich himself at the expense of the merchants who traveled between Kiev and Novgorod to the north. Solovey got many men together into his wicked fellowship. They killed and they plundered so much that within a few months few were the merchants who dared risk the road north from Kiev.

Vladimir did not know what to do. He offered arms to the merchants, but they said that, being men of peace, they would not know what to do with them. Vladimir asked the neighboring princes to help him fight Solovey, but they were all busy with varied troubles of their own. "Surely," they answered Vladimir, "your dominions are so great and so rich that you can deal with a brigand." But Vladimir could not, and he watched Kiev's prosperity dwindle from month to month.

The root of the trouble was that Solovey was no ordinary brigand. He had magic to help him. He and his fellow bandits were known to assume the shape of serpents, and to kill wayfarers with their poison. Solovey also had the terrible power of turning those who displeased him into stumps of birches. There were other fearful stories about the brigand. When matters got quieter in the south and the east, Vladimir's warriors came back to Kiev. They bluntly refused to go and fight Solovey. The markets of Kiev grew emptier and emptier until it was difficult for a cobbler to find a piece of leather to make a pair of boots, to say nothing of housewives who could not buy salt for the porridge.

Vladimir was greatly troubled. He foresaw the coming ruin of the country. He still had much gold in his treasury, but Solovey could not be bribed. Vladimir had two cunning magicians at his court, and at last he sent them northward. But their spells were not strong enough, and Solovey killed them both. There was no one else, and Vladimir began wondering if it would not be better for him to challenge the brigand in person, but his Princess implored him not to take such a terrible risk.

"I must not leave anything undone to help my people," he argued, but she said:

"You would hardly help them by getting killed."

Vladimir went to the Cathedral one evening. There he fell on his knees and prayed hard and fervently for a way to be shown to him. He came out, and an elderly pilgrim in a dusty and tattered cloak passed by. Vladimir wished him good evening and invited him to supper at the palace. The pilgrim thanked him and added:

"God has heard your prayer, my lord," and that night the Prince slept peacefully for the first time in many months.

Now there was a town in Vladimir's dominions called Murom. A hamlet, Karachaevo, clung to its outskirts. The

18

poorest inhabitants at Karachaevo were a certain Daniel and Maria. All land being drawn by lot, the least rewarding field had fallen to their share: for good rye they often had docks and thistles, and nettles sprouted where they had sown turnip seeds. They took great care of their two cows, but something was always going wrong: either a cow would die in calving, or else her milk would dry up. If a summer storm swept over Karachaevo, it was always their thatch that was struck by lightning. If a fox made an onslaught on the hamlet, it was usually their hen house he made for.

But the couple's bitterest sorrow sprang from a deeper cause than their poverty. They had an only child, a son, Ilya, whom they loved and cherished, but Ilya was born a cripple. He had passed his thirtieth year and he had never as much as moved a muscle. So sweet was his nature that he never complained except by way of expressing his grief that he could do nothing to lighten his parents' burdens. Yet it was precisely Ilya's courage and patience that enabled them to go through their own difficulties without complaining.

One summer day Daniel and Maria had to go and do some business at Murom, and Ilya, as usual, lay motionless on his trestle when three pilgrims in dusty and tattered cloaks came into the hut, crossed themselves in front of Our Lady's icon, and bowed to Ilya who said:

"Welcome, God's people, and I hope you will not think me rude in not getting up, but I have been a cripple from my birth and I cannot move. The well is at the back of the hut, and I know that my mother never forgets to hang a clean towel on the nail by the door. There is a crock of milk and some bread for your refreshment, and

I am sure my parents will be sorry to miss you."

The three pilgrims bowed again, went to wash their hands and faces, came back, and helped themselves to the milk and the bread. Ilya lay, watching them, his blue eyes smiling.

"Now," the eldest pilgrim said to him, "God reward you for your hospitality, son. Could you do us yet another kindness? We are strangers here, and we have lost our way. How do we get to the road that runs from Kiev north to Novgorod?"

"God's people," Ilya replied courteously, "I would not be even the poor Christian that I am if I were to help you find that road. No man's foot has trod it in safety for some time now. I have heard folk talk about a dreadful brigand called Solovey, and so much harm has he done that I hear life is very bitter for the Prince's people at Kiev and elsewhere. I have also heard that no warrior in the Prince's service will dare to ride against the brigand. There is such talk about the witchery he practices."

"Indeed, we know all about that wicked Solovey," replied the pilgrim quietly, "and we are here because of him. Son, you have answered our question in the right way, God bless you," and he got up, took a small flask out of the folds of his tattered gray smock, and sprinkled a few drops of pink fluid over Ilya's motionless body. The other two pilgrims bent their heads, and Ilya, his blue eyes big with wonder, watched the pink drops fall and asked no questions at all.

The eldest pilgrim stoppered the flask and touched Ilya's right shoulder.

"Get your legs clear of the bed coverings," he said, and Ilya answered:

"No limb of mine has ever moved, but since you ask, I'll try and do so because my parents always say that a guest's pleasure is the host's delight."

And Ilya moved first his right leg, then his left—very slowly and clumsily. He felt no pain whatever but he thought that his legs were made of straw.

"Stand up, Ilya," said the three pilgrims together, and again he obeyed, though it was more than strange to be standing up instead of lying down. All at once he knew that his legs had strength in them.

"Lift your arms above your head, Ilya," they told him, and he drew a deep breath and knew that strength was coming into his shoulders. He stood there, waiting for the next order, and he did not have to wait long.

There lay an enormous cudgel along the wall facing the trestle where Ilya had lain for so many years. It was heavily tipped with iron. Ilya's grandfather, still remembered for his prodigious strength, had found that cudgel by the bank of the river, and six athletic peasants had helped him drag it into the hut. So heavy it was that later nobody would have dreamed of trying to lift it.

"Take up the cudgel," said the eldest pilgrim, and Ilya instantly obeyed. It was really odd—but it cost him no effort at all: the cudgel might have been made of straw—so easily did he pick it up, and once again the pilgrim unstoppered the flask and sprinkled the cudgel with the same pink fluid.

"Carry the cudgel into the yard and swing it first with your right arm and then with your left," Ilya was told, and again that seemed easy to do, and with the second swing Ilya brought down a tall fir which stood just outside the yard gate.

21

"Turn around," said the pilgrims, and Ilya turned and saw a huge black horse, his bridle of crimson silk and chased silver, and his saddle of fine red leather, standing near the door of the hut.

"This is your mount," they told him, and the eldest of them went on, "The cudgel is your weapon and it will never let you down. Kiev is in great trouble, and you are the man to deliver it. You have been chosen for the task because of your courage and selflessness. Never once have you been known to complain of your misfortune."

"God's people," Ilya replied, "what reason had I to complain, seeing what loving parents I have?"

"Now," the eldest pilgrim went on, "mount your horse and ride southeastward. Presently you will come to a cross roads, and thee you will have to make a decision, nobody helping or prompting you. And you need not worry about your dear parents—all shall go well with them, and you will return and see them often enough, but your business now is to rescue Kiev from the peril infesting the road to the north."

Here the three pilgrims bowed and went away so quickly that it looked as though a cloud of dust had swallowed them up.

Ilya snatched at the crimson bridle and led the horse out of the gate. There he stood for a little while, his eyes tranced with pure happiness. Open skies, the wind, the golden promise of ripening corn, the running water across one of the fields, the gay embroidery of wild flowers, were all his for the first time to look at and to love. Bareheaded and unshod, nothing but a peasant's rough smock and brief linen breeches covering his body, Ilya stood there, gratitude in mind and in heart. Then he picked up the great cudgel and sprang into the saddle as easily as though he had ridden from his boyhood. Just after he had cleared the hamlet, Ilya saw his parents, who were frightened into speechlessness at the sight of him on horseback. But Ilya at once dismounted, told them all that had happened, received their blessing, and rode away down a narrow lane bordered with poppies and corn-flowers. He had no idea what awaited him beyond the fateful crossroads, but he knew that life was sweet indeed.

Presently Ilya came to the crossroads. Now he could see three paths running ahead of him, to the right, to the middle, and to the left. At the start of each path stood a stone. The one to the right had an inscription: "This way ride to your wedding," and Ilya shook his head.

"I would hardly be helping the Prince and his people if I started looking for a bride," he said to himself, and rode on to the second stone flanking the middle path. That was supposed to bring him a great fortune, and again Ilya shook his head.

"Saddlebags filled with gold would not be enough to help Kiev," he thought.

The stone to the left had a different inscription traced in big black letters:

"This way will probably lead to death."

"That is my way," Ilya decided. "For all I know, my death may be of use to Prince Vladimir and to Kiev. Ah well, it is a big thing to have felt God's free wind on one's face," and down the left path Ilya cantered, the giant cudgel held in his right hand.

At first, the going was pleasant enough. On either side stretched fields of pale green rye and gold-brown wheat, blue ribbons of cornflowers threading the corn. Well ahead loomed a vast wood of tall silver birches, their bark gleaming in the generous summer sun. The day was hot, and Ilya was glad to reach the cool shade of the wood. "Just like a bride on her wedding day," he thought, glancing at a slim sapling standing to his right, clumps of wild strawberries at its foot. The fragrance was tempting, but Ilya would not stop to pick the berries. He rode on right through the wood, until he reached a great undulating open field. Just to the left Ilya saw a lonely little hut, a bent-shouldered woman in a bright green shawl standing in the doorway. She stared hard at him, for there was a peasant—to judge by his clothes—riding a superb black horse, a jeweled bit to the bridle and a splendid saddle.

Ilya rode up and reined in. He did not like her unfriendly stare, but she wished him good day and asked if he would like a drink of milk.

"And what is your name and calling?" she added, pursing her thin lips.

"Ilya of Murom, a peasant's son," he answered. "I am in the Prince's service. How far will it be to the north road?"

"Eh?" she peered at him. "Are you trying to tell me you are for the north road?"

"I am."

"And in the Prince's service," she said mockingly. "Ah well, you can't miss it. Keep straight on." She cackled, "I'd better save my milk for some other traveler. You will find plenty of victuals once you get there, Ilya of Murom—"

And she shook a bony fist at him and vanished through the doorway. Ilya shrugged his shoulders and rode off.

2068

A fearful sight met his eyes when he reached the highest point of the common: all down its slope lay the bleached skeletons of men and of horses. Farther on, where the common ran into a thick forest of high firs, the bones were piled up in great mounds.

"Solovey's lair must be inside the wood," guessed Ilya.

At the very fringe of the wood the black horse halted and refused to move. Ilya coaxed, scolded, and beat him in turn, but the beast seemed rooted, and Ilya must needs dismount and tie him to the nearest fir. Then, the cudgel in his right hand, he entered the wood. He had not gone very far when he heard shrill laughter somewhere above him. Ilya looked up. There, perched astride a bough, sat a man dressed in green from head to foot.

"Well, so you have come to join the company over there?" He jerked a thumb toward the clearing and laughed again.

"Me?" said Ilya. "Why should I? I am a simple peasant's son. I am no knight or wealthy merchant. I come from Murom, and my name is Ilya."

"What do I care about your name?" the other broke in. "A peasant indeed, are you? Riding a horse fit for a prince? I saw you up there on the common. Now I am on guard here, and my duty is to kill anyone I see passing, and I take their gear as my due, but not their mounts—they go to the master if they are as good as yours is. And you have got nothing—not even a pair of boots!"

"A cat might leap on the moon before a peasant is seen wearing boots," Ilya replied calmly, "but I have got a stout cudgel—"

"That?" drawled the man in green. "And what use would such a clumsy thing be to me?"

"Well, now, I might show you," replied Ilya, and he swung the cudgel high above his head. The great bough cracked; the man in green tumbled down and lay, his skull broken, at Ilya's feet. Instantly two huge snakes crept from behind a tree and reared themselves up to strike at Ilya who, however, was too quick for them and dispatched them both with one deft blow of the cudgel.

So Ilya went on through the whole length of that wood. He was stopped thirty-nine times and he killed thirty-nine brigands, and his strength grew and grew with every swing of the cudgel.

At last, the wood behind him, Ilya came out on a wide road running right and left. Just ahead stood a small oak coppice. Ilya hesitated. He did not know which way to take to reach the master brigand's lair, and just at that moment he clearly heard the eldest pilgrim's voice behind him:

"Make for those oak trees. Solovey's keep is inside there. Every time you feel danger coming near, say in your heart, 'Help me,' and the cudgel will do your business for you."

Ilya turned. But there was nobody to see, and he tramped on toward the oak trees. Soon enough he saw the stone walls of a keep and several grim-faced men by the gateway. They sprang forward on seeing him, and so many they were that they succeeded in throwing Ilya down on the ground, but he clenched his fingers tight and said in his heart, "Help me."

At once the cudgel leaped out of Ilya's grasp and began striking at one man after another so swiftly that they were all killed before Ilya had time to draw a breath. Two more brigands, hurrying to join their comrades, saw it happen and hid themselves behind a huge water butt near the gateway. Ilya got up, shook the dust off his shirt and breeches, and shouted:

"Come out, both of you—I want you!"

The men in green crept out and came up to Ilya. They were shaking from chin to toe.

"Is this Solovey's lair?"

They nodded.

"Then lead me to him," Ilya ordered, "and don't imagine that you can out-trick me. I have just killed eighty snakes in the forest."

The men shook their heads hurriedly. They had no intention of doing anything of the kind. All they wanted was to run away from this terrible peasant, whose cudgel, as they thought, must have been fashioned by the devil. So they led the way into a vast courtyard. Enormous piles of plunder were lying everywhere, rare stuffs and carpets, amber and ivory and pearls, silver and golden vessels, all of it speaking of the fearful robberies carried out by Solovey and his gang of killers. Ilya clenched his fists and shouted:

"Here, have you got names, you two, or are you unchristened infidels?"

"I am Eel," stuttered the taller man of the two, and his companion stammered:

"I am Adder."

"I thought you were infidels," said Ilya. "Whoever heard of Christian folk having such names? Now then, you, Eel, and you, Adder, mind you stand on guard here in the yard. Not a bag of spices or a single pearl is to be lost unless you want to mount the gallows." And, the cudgel clasped in his right hand, Ilya mounted the steps into Solovey's hall.

There, at a high table, eating his dinner of broiled pike

and turnips, sat the terror of Kiev, a small man with shifty pale eyes and a cruel mouth. He wore red leather breeches and a white coat bespattered with gore here and there. Ilya saw those stains, and his eyes darkened with anger.

"Come up," thundered Solovey. "I have been expecting you. An owl in a bright green shawl brought me the story. Well, I want to see the magic from Murom. None to be found in Kiev, I think," and Solovey's thin mouth curved contemptuously. "Had any dinner—you magician of harrow and plow?" He did not wait for Ilya's answer but cut off a large slice of the pike and threw it across the room. It fell at Ilya's feet. He did not even look at it.

"Yes," Solovey went on, "they are all shaking and quaking in their boots in Kiev, and the Prince sent two old sorcerers to work their stupid spells on me. But mine proved far stronger, and I had the men hanged, though I got nothing for my trouble. Well, I don't mean to waste good rope on you, peasant from Murom. There is a deep river behind the keep, and drowning is good enough for such as you. Well," he roared, "can't you speak? I have given you good food, and you won't even look at it. I am ready to listen to you, and you stand there as dumb as a block of wood. I must say I don't think much of the manners taught at Murom! Can't you even thank me for my kindness—and you having murdered over fifty of my best men—"

"And how many have you murdered, Solovey?" Ilya asked softly.

"Ah, that is a question to please me. Wait, here is my tally. Why, forty-nine thousand eight hundred and twenty-four. And the plunder! I could buy up the whole of Vladimir's land!"

"No doubt, no doubt," Ilya agreed. "Well, I have seen

you, Solovey. Now will you do me one favor before I die?"

"What is it? I make no promises. Why, you might expect me to stop killing."

Ilya shook his head.

"Nobody could ever expect that from you, Solovey. No, let me have a silken cord and a good strong sack, Solovey, and let someone carry my body to Daniel and Maria at Karachaevo at the gates of Murom so that they can give their son a Christian burial. And I would like to see the cord and the sack, please, and touch both with my hand before I die."

"Well," Solovey laughed and clapped his hands. "I must say this is a very modest request."

A servant came in, and presently a thick cord of green silk and a good strong sack were brought in, and Ilya touched both with his hands. Then, clasping the cudgel, he said in his heart, "Help me," as Solovey shouted:

"Hi, you fellows outside, take the cudgel away from him and throw him into the river."

Ilya looked up.

"Kill me, Solovey, if such be your pleasure—but you cannot have me thrown into the river because you promised that my body shall be returned to Murom."

Solovey took no notice. His eyes were on fire.

"Hi," he thundered, "you dunderheads, haven't you heard me? Take that cudgel away and throw the man into the river."

But Solovey's men stood by the door and never moved. They muttered that it was no use for anyone to try and take the cudgel from Ilya.

"You cowardly donkeys," roared Solovey, "always leaving the hardest jobs to your master to do. I shall make you pay for this one day," and he rose from his chair.

Without wasting an instant Ilya swung the cudgel, but a huge snake uncoiled itself from behind Solovey's chair and warded off the blow.

"So much for the magic from Murom," laughed Solovey, gripped the snake in his right hand and made for Ilya, but the cudgel warded off the blow.

Now they were at it in grim earnest, and Ilya understood that Solovey's spells were indeed very powerful. The enormous cudgel glanced off at the least touch of the snake's fangs. The battle went on and on, and Ilya wondered if his own strength would endure it much longer. He could not but notice that he swung the cudgel less swiftly and deftly. What was even worse—he could not remember which words he must say to make the cudgel do his business for him. Something like a cloud hung over Ilya's mind, and Solovey, his own strength unspent, had no doubt of the outcome.

There came a terrible moment when Ilya's cudgel all but failed to ward off the snake, and Ilya's feet slipped on the floor. Just then he heard a familiar voice whisper behind him:

"Step to the left. Take a good aim. Say 'Help me'."

Ilya obeyed. The great cudgel cleaved the air like lightning, and the snake writhed violently, struggled out of Solovey's clutch, and fell dead on the floor. His face red with fury, the brigand whistled for another snake to come to his help, but Ilya did not waste a second. He raised his weapon high and let it fall, and the terror of Kiev, his head smashed, fell on the floor. All his loyal friends, except for Eel and Adder, screamed and at once ran off into the forest.

Ilya took the body and put it into the sack. Then he

31

ordered Eel and Adder to have a horse saddled. He loaded the beast with as much treasure as he could carry, and then rode off to Kiev.

Everybody in the city stared at a peasant in a dusty smock who came mounted on a splendid black horse, but when they learned the truth there was such rejoicing that the bells nearly deafened the people. Prince Vladimir left his hall and ran to his deliverer.

"I give you twenty-five manors as your reward and all the plunder at Solovey's palace," he said to Ilya.

"My lord," Ilya replied, "what would a peasant do with one manor, let alone twenty-five of them? But I would be glad if my father received two or three good fields and a new harrow. His got broken last autumn. And I wish for no other reward, my lord, except to be allowed always to serve you."

"Indeed, you shall," Vladimir told Ilya, and a messenger was at once sent to Murom to see that Daniel and Maria had their three good fields and a new harrow given to them.

Such, then, was the beginning of that gallant Fellowship. The story of Ilya's wonderful victory over Solovey spread up and down Vladimir's dominions, and other young men came to offer their service, and were duly knighted once their courage was proved in warding off all invaders and in fighting all the dragons and other monsters in the land. Their numbers grew and grew, but the name of Ilya of Murom always remained at their head. The Fellowship came to be known as that of the Golden Table because the Knights had their seats there, to the right and the left of the Prince's red-canopied chair.

THE SECOND TALE

Dobryna's Embassy to Khan Amryl

THE SECOND TALE

Dobryna's Embassy to Khan Amryl

THE news that valiant men were needed at Prince Vladimir's court gradually reached every town and village in the principality, including a most unimportant place called Galy. The people of Galy did not show much interest; Galy lay at some distance from Kiev, none among them had ever been there, and their business lay with their fields and what poaching they could carry on in the neighboring woods which did not belong to them.

Yet Galy had an inn kept by a widow, Liuba, who had more strings to her bow than the making and selling of mead. It was whispered that Liuba had "the gift" and that once long ago she had turned a dishonest debtor into a pig. She was not very popular, but the men of Galy had nowhere else to go for their mead, and Liuba plied a brisk enough trade.

She had one son, Dobryna, and everybody said that little good would ever come of him—so lazy he was. Once Dobryna lay for seven and a half hours under an apple tree, waiting for the fruit to fall into his lap. They said that his mother had spoiled him because she never asked for his help either in the house or in the inn. But Liuba loved Dobryna so much that few were the people who dared to criticize him in her presence.

"Early days yet," she would retort in reply to the least disparaging remark about Dobryna. "And what is there for a young man like my Dobryna to do at Galy? Do you think I would let him soil his hands with the plow and the harrow?"

People did not know what to think and they said nothing. So young Dobryna grew and grew; broad-shouldered, tall, fair, he ate, drank, slept, and knew how to keep still. It would have been difficult to say what else he could do.

The day Liuba heard about the happenings at Kiev, she locked herself in her little room upstairs, leaving the sale of mead to a servant. Liuba spent the whole morning by herself, and then she went to look for Dobryna. She found him at the bottom of the orchard by the river bank. He sat, dangling his shapely bare legs in the water, and he had the air of someone who had not a care in the world.

"Dobryna," Liuba said very solemnly, "your great chance has come. You will wear shining armor, ride a splendid horse, and eat your dinner off gold. You are going to Kiev. Prince Vladimir is in need of young men, and you are the finest young man in the whole principality. I would put poison into anyone's drink if they said that you were not."

Dobryna had got up on seeing his mother. Now he sat down again and yawned.

"Whatever are you talking about, Mother? Why should I go to Kiev?"

"To fight the Tartar and any dragon you may meet."

"Fight a dragon?" Dobryna's grey eyes flew wide with wonder and fear. "Mother, I have never fought even a beetle in my life. Why, I would die of fright if ever I met a dragon—" Dobryna spread his hands on the warm silken grass and added, "I am all right here, Mother, with you. You have never wanted me to do anything."

"I was waiting for a chance. It has come."

"Kiev is almost at the other end of the world. I would be so tired before I got there."

Liuba retorted angrily:

"I have been hoping for fame to come to you all these years, and this is how you behave. I would not allow you to work in the fields because I knew you were meant for better things, and is this the way you repay me for the care I have spent on you? Take care, Dobryna! I love you dearly, but if you were to cross my will, I could easily turn *you* into a beetle. And I shall do so if you shame me. There is a crowd of men drinking at our place, and I have told them all that you are going to Kiev, and go you shall."

Dobryna was frightened.

"And I thought you loved me," he said sadly.

"Of course I do. You are my only son. I have let you spend many years in idleness, but that is all over. You have passed your twenty-fifth birthday, and it is time you were famous."

"Famous?" cried Dobryna. "Mother, I'll be killed if a dragon as much as looks at me."

"No dragon will ever hurt you," retorted Liuba and pulled a blue silk kerchief out of the folds of her kirtle. "Hold this kerchief in your right hand between the thumb and the forefinger, wave it gently, and wish a wish. This will be your shield, my son," and, seeing Dobryna hesitate, Liuba added promptly, "otherwise I'll turn you into a beetle."

Dobryna groaned. He had no wish to be turned into anything, least of all a beetle, and the blue silk kerchief certainly teased his imagination. He scrambled up to his feet and stretched out his hand for it.

"Mother, will it do just everything I wish?"

"Of course," Liuba replied, and Dobryna's eyes lit up with sudden mischief.

"So if I hold it the way you told me to do and wish you to be turned into a grasshopper, it would happen, wouldn't it?"

In a flash Liuba hid the blue kerchief in her kirtle.

"Ah, you thought you would outwit me?" she cried. "No, son. I've got another kerchief for you—but I shall not give it to you unless you swear you will not use it until you stand facing the enemy. Do you swear it?"

"I do," said Dobryna, "and I never meant to turn you into a grasshopper, Mother."

Liuba put a much smaller kerchief of soft crimson silk between his hands.

"Wave it to the right and to the left when danger threatens you."

"And what happens then? Does my wish come true?"

"You'll find that out for yourself," Liuba told him.

Dobryna sighed as he followed his mother into the house. There he found that she had got things ready for him; a blue embroidered shirt, white linen breeches, a square fur cap and a stout ash stick—such being Liuba's idea of a knight's equipment. She also let him have a little money and a bundle of food.

"Mind you keep the kerchief hidden out of sight unless you are in danger," said Liuba. "Then wave it first to the right and then to the left."

"And how do I know when I am in danger?" Dobryna wanted to know, and Liuba promptly told him to stop pretending he was a fool.

Most reluctantly he took to the road. It was at the very height of summer, and a breeze sang in the ripening wheat, but he never looked at the fields round about him. He entered a wood, its floor enameled with tiny wild flowers of all the colors known to man, and Dobryna, though he had not walked more than an hour, decided it was time to eat and rest. He ate heartily and he slept for thirteen hours.

Dobryna did not hurry. It took him several days to get to Kiev. He had faced no dangers and met with no adventures on the way. He was footsore and a little bored by the time he reached the city. Its marvelous buildings made little impression on him. "Surely our little houses at Galy must be much more snug in the winter," he said to himself. "Well, I suppose I must go and see the Prince, and he will be the first to say that I'd better turn back home at once. What does a fellow like me want with fame?"

The palace being open to all, Dobryna found no difficulty in entering Vladimir's hall. The Prince, his lady, nobles and Knights were at dinner, but the splendor of the appointments, the glitter of gold and jewels did not abash Dobryna. He walked up to the golden table, the fur cap held between his hands, bowed to Vladimir and his lady, and said loudly:

"My mother said I was to come here to wear shining armor, ride a splendid horse, and eat my dinner off gold, and I have come."

The Princess put down her jeweled goblet and raised a napkin to her mouth. Her husband stopped eating and stared. So did everybody else, and here and there were heard ripples of subdued laughter. Dobryna stood well over six feet, he was broad of shoulder and his fair beard reached almost to his chest, but all of them thought that he had spoken in the manner of a little boy repeating a hard-learned lesson.

"And what can you do?" Vladimir asked, and Dobryna took a little time before he replied:

"I have never done anything except sleep, eat, drink and sit still. I have once ridden the priest's cow, and I suppose I could ride a horse. They both have four legs," he added politely.

This time the laughter was anything but subdued until the Prince's frown put a stop to it.

"Well, do you think there are things in Kiev that must get done?" he asked, and Dobryna stared at his bare feet.

"How can I tell? They work the land at Galy where I come from, and they also drink mead at my mother's inn. But there are many more people in Kiev and I suppose many more things are done, but I would not know. My mother said I would come to fame by going to Kiev."

Vladimir leaned back in his red-canopied chair. His wife was hard put to it to conceal her laughter, but Dobryna stood unperturbed, clutching his fur cap.

"Send him back to his fool of a mother, my lord," suggested one of the Knights.

At once Dobryna dropped the cap and, fists clenched, rushed at the speaker. In an instant Dobryna's enormous hands were at the other's throat, and the great hall rang with a furious voice:

"Call my mother that name again, and I will kill you!"

The nobles were aghast. The Knights leapt to their feet, but Vladimir's voice rose above the tumult:

"Stop at once unless you want to be thrown into the dungeons. How dare you start a brawl in my presence?"

Dobryna loosened his clutch and staggered back, his

eyes almost black with fury, his face crimson. The fur cap still lay on the bright mosaic floor, and a great stillness fell in the hall. All of them wished they might look at their Prince and yet they dared not; Vladimir's temper could be as savage as a winter storm, and even his wife knew she could not interfere.

They all waited. The Prince sat motionless, his right hand cupping his chin. And Dobryna's face was no longer crimson: it looked almost as white as the Princess's silken napkin. He well guessed what he had done: it was a terrible offense to start fighting anyone in Vladimir's presence.

The Prince looked at him very hard.

"There is one thing you can do," he said at last in so mild a voice that everybody breathed in relief. "Defend your mother! It was fine. It was gallant. Also it was foolhardy. You risked your neck. Did you know that?"

"I could have done no other," Dobryna said stubbornly.

"You are to stay here," decided the Prince, "I need young men like you."

That very day Dobryna found himself at school. The Knights taught him to ride, to use the bow, the pike and the lance. They taught him many other things. At first Dobryna hated it all, but little by little he felt drawn into their life of endless, tiring activities. So strong was he that none among Vladimir's Knights dared provoke him to a quarrel.

Some time passed, and they reported to the Prince that Dobryna had made excellent progress.

"He is very quick of wit, my lord," they added, "the only trouble is that, having done nothing all his life, he now wants to do everything."

"Well," said Vladimir, "I had better set him a task. If

he does it well, I shall knight him."

He had already decided what Dobryna was to do before winning the golden spurs, the latter being a Knight's first mark of distinction.

At the very beginning of his reign, Vladimir had lost a battle against Khan Amryl, and much to the shame of all the people of Kiev, the Prince had to send him tribute once every three years. The tribute consisted of two hundred silver spoons, a big jar of honey, five pieces of red silk and a small bag of pearls. When Dobryna heard about the tribute, he was angry.

"It is shameful to have to carry such good stuff to the Tartar."

"Ah," they explained to him, "the Prince lost that battle before our Fellowship was founded, and he promised on his honor that the tribute should be paid. He cannot break such a promise."

"Is it for the Khan's lifetime?" Dobryna wanted to know.

"It is, but you must remember that you go as the Prince's emissary and you must not kill the Khan."

"I am not going to kill him," answered Dobryna.

He had leave to go and see his mother. He told her about his mission and asked that the blue kerchief should be given to him. Liuba refused.

"I might give it you the day you are made a knight."

"At least, tell me what the red kerchief can do for me," Dobryna begged.

"Ah, that is for you to find out once you have waved it first to the right and then to the left," Liuba replied and sent him off with her blessing.

When Dobryna returned to Kiev, it was time for him

42

to start on his mission. The silver spoons, the honey, the red silk and the pearls were all packed.

"Will you have three men-at-arms to ride with you?" they asked him, and Dobryna shook his head.

"I am going alone."

At some distance from Kiev he stopped, dismounted, and dug a deep hole by the side of the road. There Dobryna buried the tribute and marked the spot carefully.

Then he rode on and on until he came to a vast plain dotted all over with white tents, and some twenty Tartars ran towards him. Their courteous manner rather took him aback; he had expected them to be hostile.

"What is your pleasure, Sir Knight?" they asked him, and Dobryna felt flattered.

"To see Khan Amryl," he replied, and they at once led him to the Khan's tent in the middle of the camp.

Dobryna bowed as he came in and looked about, his curiosity mounting. He had never seen such a place in his life. The great tent, carpeted in thick pink silk, had no furniture except a number of blue and green velvet cushions. Khan Amryl, a small shriveled man with narrow black eyes and a slit of a mouth, was sitting on the ground. He wore a red and blue striped gown of rich Persian silk, and a brown bear cub lay at his feet.

"You come nearly two months late," he said in a raucous voice, "and where is the tribute?"

"Not very far from here," Dobryna replied, bowed once again, and glanced at the bear cub. "Sir, I wonder if you would be kind enough to call one of your scribes."

Khan Amryl's face darkened.

"What do you want with a scribe? Where are the silver spoons, the honey, the red silk and the pearls?"

43

"Sir," Dobryna said earnestly, "since you have waited nearly two months, will you be generous enough to wait for less than an hour?"

Khan Amryl did not look like a man who could be generous even for the space of a minute. But he clapped his hands, and a soldier, a wicked curved knife stuck into his belt, came at once.

"Fetch my senior scribe," ordered the Khan, "and fetch my treasurer to count the silver spoons and the pearls. Where has the tribute been left?"

"Lord," answered the soldier, "we saw the gentleman ride into the camp. He carried no saddlebags. He came alone."

"Is this a joke?" shouted Khan Amryl. "Where is the tribute?"

"Not far from here, sir," Dobryna said for the second time, and the Khan's mouth went into a cruelly thin line.

"You have never brought it at all," he shouted. "Vladimir has broken his promise, and this very evening I march on Kiev."

Dobryna said nothing.

"Fetch the senior scribe," Amryl ordered the soldier, "and the executioner, too. I am at war with Vladimir, and this man is an enemy." His eyebrows bristling, he turned to Dobryna: "You have about fifteen minutes left. I suppose it is your will you wish to make. Well, I'll be generous and let you make it."

The scribe came in with his style, inkwell and tablets of polished bone. The executioner followed, carrying a brightly gleaming axe.

"It is my last will, sir," Dobryna agreed, and began dictating:

"I hereby bequeath to Vladimir, Prince of Kiev and

all adjoining lands my two hundred silver spoons, my jar of honey, my five pieces of red silk and the four hundred and seventy-five pearls in a small white velvet bag, it being due to me from the said Prince Vladimir, and I also waive my future rights to receive such a due from him and his successors according to law." And, having finished, Dobryna said, "I have no other goods or chattels to leave."

It took the Khan quite a few minutes to take in the meaning of "the will." He leapt to his feet and roared at the executioner:

"Behead him at once!"

But Dobryna lost no time. He whisked out the little red kerchief and waved it to the right and then to the left, his heart beating wildly. He had no idea what his mother's gift could do. Suddenly the axe fell from the executioner's upraised hand.

"Do you want to lose your own head?" Khan Amryl stormed at the man. "Up with the axe! Off with this villain's head!"

"Lord," stammered the unfortunate executioner, "my hands have turned to straw. I could not lift as much as a button from the floor."

"Fool!" thundered the Khan, rushed forward, and snatched at the axe, and once again Dobryna's red kerchief went right and went left, and the axe fell out of the Khan's hands.

"Now, sir," said Dobryna, "from all I have heard, you won that battle by a trick, and you have lost its fruits by another. I might turn your bear cub into a beetle, but I'd rather not. All I want is your signature at the bottom of this writing. I know you couldn't hold the style, but I'll guide your hand."

And, carefully holding the red kerchief in his left hand, Dobryna took the Khan's right hand into his, and guided it until a clumsy signature appeared at the bottom of the tablet.

So pleased was Dobryna with his achievement that he never noticed the sign made by the Khan to the scribe who, at once guessing his master's wishes, snatched the red kerchief out of Dobryna's left hand. In an instant the Khan and the executioner recovered their lost strength, and so amazed were they at being able to use their hands again that neither of them thought about the axe still lying on the floor. They fell on Dobryna, the executioner clutching his knees, the Khan trying to reach his waist, and the scribe, in an effort to snatch at Dobryna's hands, let drop the red kerchief.

Such a wrath welled up in Dobryna that his fists were turned to iron, and he killed the executioner with one blow and the scribe with another. Once again the red kerchief was between his fingers. He remembered that he must not kill the Khan and he merely waved the kerchief in front of him, and the Khan was rooted to the floor. Then Dobryna stooped for the tablet of polished bone and ran out of the tent.

Outside, many soldiers rushed towards him, but Dobryna waved the kerchief from right to left, and their feet too were rooted to the ground. He leaped into the saddle and his horse flew on wings.

Khan Amryl honored his signature. Vladimir knighted Dobryna and rewarded him with all the tribute he had buried in the field. At Galy, Liuba went on selling her mead, and she wore a necklace of four hundred and seventy-five pearls every day.

THE THIRD TALE

Potok's Dancing and the Snakes

THE THIRD TALE

Potok's Dancing and
the Snakes

THIS is what happened at a time when all the people of
Kiev held high festival because a son was born to Prince
Vladimir and his lady. On the day of the child's christen-
ing, his father gave a traditional feast. All the merchants,
artisans, and less important folk had their share of the
good things in the immense forecourt of the palace. In the
main hall, the Prince was feasting with all the distinguished foreigners then staying in the city, the nobles, and
the Knights. It fell on a bright day in May, and the long
golden table set out with goblets and dishes of gold
and silver was so dazzling that people seated at some distance from it had to screen their eyes from the splendor.
The meal, begun soon after noon, did not end till long
after sunset. It started with spiced porridge and finished
with curiously shaped honey cakes baked by a clever cook
from an island on the Baltic. The cakes were made like
castles, ships, horses, bears, and fishes, and there was one
to represent Vladimir, his Princess, and their child seated
on the triple throne, its canopy dusted with gold.

The sun had set, and servants lit thick wax candles in
tall wooden sticks studded with pear-shaped pearls. The
pudding had long since been eaten, but the guests did not
move because they might not leave unless Vladimir gave
a sign of dismissal, and he did not wish the feast to come
to an end so soon.

"Will you play a merry dance tune?" he called out to

51

his musicians, who at once began tuning their *gously*, tri-angular-shaped string instruments. With the first notes, Potok rose from this bench, looked at the Prince, who nodded, and the Knight left the dais for the floor of the hall.

The entire assembly burst out clapping. The Kievans were famous for their dancing, and Potok of the Golden Table was known to be the finest dancer in the land. It was said that his grace and skill carried enough magic to comfort the most sorrowful heart. No wonder that Vladimir's guests clapped and cheered, and little did they know what Potok's skill was to achieve that night!

He stood there, tall and broad-shouldered, in a fine white shirt open at the throat, pleated blue breeches and boots of soft green leather. His mouth was smiling, his brown eyes dancing with merriment, and he looked a true Knight indeed. It so happened that it was his own feast-day, and on the way to church that very morning Potok had met a soothsayer.

"This will be a great day for you, Potok."

"Why so? There is nobody to rescue and nobody to fight. Our shields, axes and pikes have lain in the Prince's anteroom these many weeks. I heard Ilya of Murom grumble that our arms might go rusty indeed unless something were to happen."

"I was not thinking of any battles, Potok," the soothsayer had replied. "There is your dancing."

But now it was evening and Potok had forgotten all about the soothsayer. He stood on his points, his whole body awakening to the urgency of the music. The *gousliars* quickened the tempo, Potok threw back his head, set his arms akimbo, and was off into the first movement of the *triepak*.

Marvelous dancer that he was, Potok put all of himself into the dance. Every movement he made and the music were completely at one. Often enough he had entertained his Prince's guests after a banquet, and none among them would have desired a finer entertainment. That evening he certainly did not disappoint them.

But with the very first step taken, Potok sensed—however dimly—that his dancing was somehow different. Superb as ever, it seemed an answer to a challenge, something like delicate mockery in the face of a peril he could not see as yet. His right leg curved at the knee, his left in the air, his arms high above his head, Potok felt as though he were no longer in that splendid and familiar hall, with the Prince and the guests for audience. He felt as though he were elsewhere, far away from the palace, and dancing to a command given him not by his Prince but by someone else. Potok could not understand any of it, but it filled him with gladness and with pride, and all he knew was that he must not stop.

Presently, some of the candles began burning low. The guests, however entranced they had been with Potok's dancing, took to casting occasional glances at the Golden Table. At last, Vladimir's voice was heard ringing all over the hall. He bade a fair and peaceful night to his guests, rose and offered his arm to the Princess, and all those present bowed and left the hall. Such was the custom at Vladimir's court.

Potok alone did not seem to hear the Prince's voice. The musicians went, and the candles guttered one by one, but Potok did not need either music or light for his business. He danced on and on, and somewhere a corner of his consciousness kept telling him that he was being drawn nearer and nearer to the threshold of an important task.

53

So Potok danced his way out of the great hall, across the immense courtyard, into St. Sophia's Square, down the Street of Wisdom to the Dnieper Gate. Kiev was fast asleep by that time. Here and there, a shutter moved, a tousled head looked out, and a voice, slurred with sleep, was heard saying that the Prince's wine and mead must have flowed liberally indeed to make a Knight dance his way home.

And there was Potok dancing at the Dnieper Gate all barred and bolted for the night. The watch, carrying torches, came down from their turret, marveled at the Knight's skill, and unbarred the gates as though someone had commanded them to do so. Potok thanked the men with a smile and a courteous word, and there he was dancing his way down the steep shrub-covered hill to the banks of the Dnieper. The moon rode out from behind a cloud and silvered both land and water. To the right of the hill glimmered the lights from the Abbey of the Caves where the monks were getting ready for their night devotions, and Potok wished he might turn towards the Abbey gates and join the saintly men at their singing, but he knew that his business was not with the monks.

Soon he reached the river bank at a spot well away from the busy wharves and jetties. There ran the Dnieper, queen among rivers, moonlight rippling the water now with shimmering green, now with silver. There, Potok stopped abruptly, as though obeying an order.

He had danced for hours, and he did not feel in the least tired. Standing very still, he wondered what was going to happen, and he remembered the old soothsayer he had met in the morning.

The world was very quiet. There were hardly any

sounds except the breath of the wind among the willows, faint echoes of singing far, far behind him, and an occasional screech of an owl from the great wood on the opposite bank. When the moon glided behind another cloud, the dark was so thick that for a moment Potok could not tell land from water.

But that darkness did not last. Again the moon rose clear of clouds, and then Potok saw something that for an instant made his blood freeze.

The prow of an enormous barge appeared from behind a bend of the river, and that barge was manned by huge glittering snakes. Soon enough another barge glided past the bend, and a third, and a fourth, and a fifth. Indeed, there were so many barges that Potok soon lost all count of them. Never had he imagined that such a number of reptiles lived in the world. He knew, of course, that Ilya of Murom had once slain eighty of them, and Dobryna and others had accounted for a good many more, but here they were as numerous as the sands on the seashore.

Seen by moonlight, those red-painted barges suggested something fashioned in the depths of hell. Each snake held a long oar in its fangs, and at the prow of each barge stood a monster, its scales a dazzling gold-green, its huge fangs thrust forward as though it were ready to strike.

For some moments Potok stood bemused, and then he heard the scraping of wood against iron. The horde meant to land, and here he stood alone, even his axe and spear left behind. Were he to run all the way, he would never be in time to warn the city of the terrible peril. He supposed that the monsters came from the Bald Mountain at some distance from Kiev where a community of witches were known to live.

55

But Potok did not waste much time on reflection. Later he never could tell exactly how it happened, but there he was—dancing his way right down to the bank already crowded with the horrible monsters, their scales gleaming now orange, now gold-green. Down and down Potok danced his way, and an enormous snaked reared itself on its tail and hissed at him in a human voice:

"Ah, here we all are—come to avenge the Queen Witch's daughter because your Prince preferred that Anna of Greece to her. The Queen Witch took more than a year to make her spell perfect, and there is nothing you can do against it. It is a pity that you will not see us ravage Kiev, but you are just big enough for my youngest son's breakfast."

"Goodness," Potok said mildly, "such a breakfast might choke him."

"You need not waste your breath on impertinence before you die—" hissed the snake angrily, and Potok laughed.

He laughed because just at that moment he distinctly heard the urgent music of the *triepak* somewhere above his head. Off he was again! Each time he raised his arms to the moonlit sky, five snakes fell dead. Each time he brought his left leg up, ten monsters were coiled in death, and they died hissing so terribly that the Queen Witch on the Bald Mountain began tearing her hair in anguish. Now she knew that her spell had not been powerful enough against the might of Vladimir's Fellowship.

Potok went on dancing until the very last monster was slain. By daybreak, the entire width of the river was covered with their corpses.

Then Potok drew a deep breath, stretched himself on

57

the soft lush grass, and sank into such deep sleep that he slept the whole day through. Only at sunset did his companions find him. Speechless, they stared at the bodies of the snakes. They could not count them. Then they roused Potok and brought him back to Kiev, where Prince Vladimir sent for his goldsmith and had a great diamond fixed to Potok's right spur in reward for his courage.

Aliosha's Visit
to the Bald Mountain

THE FOURTH TALE

Aliosha's Visit
to the Bald Mountain

It was from the Bald Mountain that the snakes sailed down the Dnieper to attack Kiev, and they were all killed by Potok. Now the Bald Mountain was an oddly-shaped hill to the northwest of the city. Its name explained itself: not a tree or a shrub grew on it, nor was there any grass to be seen. For all the world, the Bald Mountain might have been likened to a huge cake taken too soon out of the oven. It was supposed to be hollow inside, though nobody had ever seen any opening. Indeed, it would have been extraordinary if anyone had done so—the people of Kiev were convinced that the Queen Witch, known as Baba Yaga, and her numerous household lived inside the Bald Mountain. It was a place to be avoided and never even looked at. The way to it led through a great silver birch wood which was also shunned by the people, though no witch had ever been seen there.

Now Baba Yaga and her minions were constantly occu- pied in annoying the people of Kiev. They flew by night, they stole brooms, besoms and pokers, they blighted crops, and tore tiles off roofs. Yet all these were, so to speak, minor irritations. The arrival of the barges manned by vicious snakes was quite a different matter.

When all the festivities in connection with Potok's vic- tory were ended, Vladimir called the Knights together to discuss a plan for putting a stop to such mischief in the future.

61

It was a formal meeting, and Vladimir wore his gold brocade mantle. The Knights sat to the right and to the left of him, their helmets on the table before them. It fell on a very sultry day. The skies over Kiev were turning lilac-pink to the west, a sure sign of a storm soon to break, and the Knights were very thirsty. But they knew that neither food nor drink would be brought in until the matter was settled, and they hoped that it would not take long.

The Prince lost no time in coming to the point and concluded:

"We have repulsed the Tartars often enough. Shall it be said that this beautiful city fell prey to a handful of wicked women?"

The Knights sat pensive. This was not the kind of an exploit they were likely to relish. Even a dragon, whatever his tricks, was an enemy they could respect, but a witch . . . Some of them shrugged, others shook their heads, and all kept silent until Ilya of Murom muttered:

"My lord, I have no stomach for such a business. Witches and womenfolk—I fight shy of the whole lot of them."

Dobryna murmured:

"Indeed, my lord, this is hardly a task for the Fellowship."

"What about our Potok dancing at the foot of the Bald Mountain?" suggested someone else, and Potok shook his head.

Other voices were heard, all equally vague. It seemed obvious that the matter of the Bald Mountain did not interest the Knights, and the Prince frowned.

"I asked for your counsel. You have none to give me. It looks as though your Prince will have to ride to the Bald Mountain himself—"

At once all the Knights leaped to their feet.

"Never, my lord—"

"We are truly ashamed—"

"My lord, we are all ready to go—"

"Choose anyone among us—"

Vladimir leaned back in his high-backed red-cushioned chair, glanced from one flushed face to another, and said softly:

"Well, then, I choose Aliosha," and the most handsome Knight among them at once laid his hand on his heart in token of ready assent.

Aliosha was handsome indeed. His hair fell in soft pale gold curls, his blue eyes had curious depths to them, his smile, as they all said, made the sun rise on the bleakest wintry day. There was always a sense of summer about Aliosha. Strong and courageous, he also had a gift which singled him out everywhere. He would take his harp even into battle, and the tunes he played were said to remove poison out of a serpent's sting. Even nightingales were known to stop singing when they heard Aliosha's music, and no bear, wolf, or wild boar had ever done him any hurt. His music enchanted insects, birds and animals.

And now the business of the Bald Mountain fell to his lot.

The people of Kiev were stupefied when they saw their best-loved Knight ride down the Street of Wisdom. They knew that he was bound for the Bald Mountain. But he rode alone, no Knights to succor him in peril; he wore his white-plumed helmet but, except for his shield, he carried no armor. The little harp was tied to his back with cords of crimson silk, and he rode away, singing one of his own songs about the beauty of a mountain stream.

Aliosha came to the Dnieper and crossed by the ford. In

about two hours he reached the edge of the silver birch forest. Here, he reined in his horse, untied the crimson silk cords, and laid the small harp across the saddle. But for the helmet and the shield, he looked very much like a knight riding to meet the lady he loved. He rode through the wood at an easy pace, and soon came to a small clearing, with the Bald Mountain rising beyond, sun rays slanting across its dull brown-veined slopes. Aliosha dismounted, led his horse to a brook, and watered him well.

"Now for the merry meeting," he murmured, and strode across the open field, the little harp slung from his right arm.

It did not take him long to reach the foot of the Bald Mountain. He walked right round it three times, and nowhere could he see any opening. At last, he sat down, wiped his forehead, and said to himself:

"I wonder if all their doors are sealed by daytime? Do I have to sit here until the evening?"

Aliosha had a leather flask of mead and some bread and cold bacon. He ate and drank, and he waited. Presently his keen eyes, which never missed the least troubling of the grass by the wind, saw the soil on a slope of the mountain move gently to the right and then to the left at the distance of about ten or twelve feet above the ground. For all the world it seemed as though someone from within were cutting into it.

"Ah," said Aliosha and waited.

He did not have to wait very long. First there appeared a narrow crack in the mountainside; then the slit widened more and more, and then it looked as though a door were opened, and through it appeared one of the most repulsive creatures Aliosha had ever seen. Her face was dirty, her eyes yellow, her long matted hair seemed full of cobwebs

64

and of dust. She wore an orange cloak trimmed with bright blue, and the harsh colors made her even more repulsive. Her toothless mouth grinned at Aliosha.

"Now, if I have not opened the door too high for you," she chuckled, "but, there, my eyes are not what they used to be. You'll have to wait, my handsome Knight, till I fetch a ladder." She added with another hideous chuckle, "Welcome to the Bald Mountain! We have such a feast ready for you!"

"Have you?" Aliosha spoke carelessly. "So you were expecting me, were you?"

"Since before you were born, my dear one," chuckled the witch, "and you are the first of them. All the others will come in their turn."

"Why do you think so?"

"Of course, they will come—just to find out what could have happened to their dear Aliosha. I assure you that there will be one feast after another. Why, her Majesty has been sitting up at night thinking how best to welcome Prince Vladimir's bold Knights!"

"Ah, she has, has she?" Aliosha laughed. "Well, why don't you fetch the ladder?"

"I will, I will," she mumbled and vanished.

Evidently the witch did not have to go far to fetch the ladder. In less than two minutes it appeared, and Aliosha, a green-booted foot on the lowest rung, flung back his head and warned the wtich not to play any tricks on him.

"As though I would dare to do any such thing! Why, the Queen would roast me alive if I as much as thought of it!"

"I'd hate to have you for my dinner," muttered Aliosha, and began scaling the ladder.

He reached the top, and the witch stepped aside. Seen

closer, she looked more horrible than ever, and Aliosha thought:

"Come to think of it, I have yet to hear of a handsome witch, and to think that dreadful Baba Yaga imagined that our Prince could marry her daughter!"

And he said aloud:

"Now take me to your Queen. I have business with her."

"Of course, I'll take you to the Queen," mumbled the witch, "but wait a moment, my dear one. Handsome you are and young you are, but there is dust on your boots, and the Queen is particular. Here, let me brush them—"

Aliosha could never account for what happened. At one moment there was the witch stooping to dust his boots. The next, her arms free of the folds of the orange cloak, she gripped his right hand so viciously that he could not but loosen his hold on the harp, and the witch grabbed it.

"Here, you old hag," he shouted, but at that very moment the opening closed in, and he found himself in inky darkness. He heard the witch's chuckle, and threshed the air with his arms, but he could not catch her. He heard the running of many feet, and then he felt hands which were as cold as fish scales clutch at his helmet, shoulders, arms and feet. Aliosha struggled wildly and blindly but it was no use—there were far too many witches, and such a fury at being bested by a horde of hags swept over Aliosha that he lost his senses.

When, stirring out of his coma, Aliosha opened his eyes, he had to blink, so dazzling was the light around him. He lay on the floor in an enormous cavern, lit by a great many torches. Up and down the cavern danced an assembly of the most ill-favored creatures Aliosha had ever seen, their matted hair falling right down to their knees, their

orange cloaks wild in the torchlight. In the middle, on a throne made of bones and covered with undressed bear skins, sat Baba Yaga, her tresses reaching down to her ankles, toads and snakes embroidered in silver on her black cloak. She had a twisted brass serpent for her crown, and a live snake for her scepter. Her eyes were blazing with fury, and she looked so terrible that Aliosha decided that the less he looked at her the better it would be for him.

He had taken part in many grim battles and faced more dangers than he could count. But now for the first time he wondered if he would see the daylight again. The little harp had always been his best weapon, and there it lay on the floor, at no great distance from where he was, but the witches had tethered him with stout ropes and put two heavy iron bars across his chest and across his feet. Both bars were secured to the ground by huge iron rings. Aliosha could not move a muscle.

How they laughed and jeered when they saw him open his eyes, but Baba Yaga struck the floor with her scepter, and all was silence. Then she leaned forward and shook a bony fist at Aliosha.

"One of your company danced and sent all my dear snakes to their death," she hissed, "and now you dare come here! Well, we have got you."

Aliosha said nothing. People, animals, birds, and insects were his friends, but it seemed that he had come to a place where no friends might be found.

"Yes," Baba Yaga went on, "we have got you, and I mean to feast on you. Have you anything to say?"

"You might not find me to your taste, Madam," Aliosha replied, "because mine is christened flesh."

"Well, I'll tell them to put plenty of magic herbs into

68

the caldron," Baba Yaga said pleasantly and smacked her lips. "Then I'll send your helmet and your skull to Kiev to teach them what it means to insult Baba Yaga! My darling daughter—with one hundred and thirty-five powerful spells for her dowry—found not good enough for that Prince of yours!" Here Baba Yaga gnashed her teeth and her eyes flashed fire. "Well, have you anything to say before they begin to cook you?"

Aliosha hesitated.

"I suppose you will grant me my very last wish?"

Baba Yaga scowled and said cautiously:

"That would depend."

"Just three short minutes to say good-by to life on my little harp."

At those words such an uproar broke out in the cavern that Aliosha would have stopped his ears if his hands were not roped together. The witches danced and leaped round about Baba Yaga's throne, and they shouted:

"Your Majesty, refuse it!"

"His music is magic!"

"He means to destroy us, Madam!"

"Baba Yaga, we are undone!"

The Queen listened for a few moments. Then her own voice drowned the mad cacophony:

"Silence, you fools! Do you think I don't know everything there is to know about the man's magic? Do you imagine I have no stronger spells of my own? Keep quiet unless you want me to turn you all into besoms and pokers!"

At once such a stillness fell on the cavern that you would have thought all the witches had stopped breathing. Then Baba Yaga laid her scepter on the floor, folded her hands, and began screaming an incantation in a language Aliosha did not know. At the very first word everybody present fell to the ground and remained motionless. Still wailing at the top of her voice, Baba Yaga rose from her throne, picked up her scepter, and walked three times round and round Aliosha's little harp.

He watched, blood almost freezing in his veins. He could not understand a word of it all, but he knew well that every word was charged with evil, and he held his breath.

Baba Yaga stopped, went back to her throne, and all the witches rose to their feet, their faces much dirtier than before.

"Untie the man," ordered Baba Yaga, "and let him have his little harp. And you need not look like so many mice in a trap," she added angrily, "I have put such a spell on that harp that its magic is of as much use as last winter's snow."

The creatures' hands were shaking violently as they began untying the cords and dragging the heavy iron bars off Aliosha's body. He got up, stretched his arms, picked up the little harp, and his supple fingers swept over the strings. It was no spring melody, or a brave battle tune, still less a love song that Aliosha began playing. It was a slow and solemn air, a prayer he had set to music the day Vladimir knighted him, a prayer to withstand and to shake off all assaults of evil.

At the very first sound Baba Yaga leaped from her throne, black fury smoldering in her eyes, but it was too late: Aliosha's virtue had not been put to sleep by the terrible incantation. In less than two minutes not a witch in the cavern but lay dead on the floor, and Aliosha played his way out into God's free air. But he did not consider his task was finished. Standing well away from the Bald Mountain, he played on and on. Slowly, very slowly, the Bald Mountain began sinking until its top was leveled down to the ground, and Aliosha went, found his horse, and rode back to Kiev.

When the story of the exploit was known, the people went mad with joy; they rushed to the palace and threw bunches of flowers all over the forecourt. A *Te Deum* was sung at the Cathedral, and one of Vladimir's minstrels composed a song in Aliosha's honor, but the young Knight was so tired that he fell asleep during the banquet given by the Prince.

THE FIFTH TALE

Young Michael
and an Uninvited Guest

THE FIFTH TALE

Young Michael
and an Uninvited Guest

It happened that Ignatius, one of the Knights of the Golden Table, fell ill. He had performed many gallant feats and had a diamond on his right spur. Now his sight was clouded, his virtue grew thin, and his arms ached when he tried to wield his axe. He asked Prince Vladimir to release him from service.

"I have a son, Michael, growing up. When he has come to his manhood, I will certainly send him to court."

Vladimir consented, but rather reluctantly. All the Knights happened to be fighting far away, and now there was a Tartar Khan, one Udol, who threatened Kiev.

One day Princess Anna was in her garden picking marigolds for a cordial against fever when her women cried out:

"My lady! My lady!"

Anna turned, and there on the bench under her favorite elm sat the ugliest little man she had ever seen, his black eyes full of malice and his mouth a slit. He wore a brown coat reaching down to his ankles, and his feet were out of all proportion to his body: a yardstick would have fitted between toe and heel. Those monstrous feet were shod in dusty white boots with silver tassels. So repulsive did the man look that Anna staggered back. Then she controlled her horror and asked haughtily:

"How dare you come into the Princess's private garden?"

The little man grinned and became uglier than ever.

"Not so fast, my proud lady, not so fast. It is against your own customs to be rude to a guest."

"A guest?" echoed the Princess angrily. "I am sure that my lord has never invited you."

"No more he has. I have invited myself. I am Khan Udol, my lady, and I have come to make Prince Vladimir give me what I have wanted for some time."

"Indeed, and what is it that you want?"

"Fishing rights in the Dnieper and his niece Lubava in marriage."

"The fishing rights are not for my lord to dispose of. They belong to him jointly with all his people. And our niece Lubava is a Christian. Never could she marry an infidel!"

"Ah," Khan Udol grinned again, "we shall talk about it later. Now I happen to be very hungry."

The Princess answered him with a proud look, signed to her ladies to follow her, and left the garden.

It was extraordinary, but the palace seemed empty. Anna found her husband in the great hall all by himself. She did not know it, but the men-at-arms and all the servants, even the Prince's cup bearer, had hidden themselves in the cellars on seeing Udol appear at the gates.

"My lord," Anna said to Vladimir, "have the watch fallen asleep? Have all the city gates been left open? And is there nobody to guard us under our own roof? Khan Udol is in my garden. He wants a dinner. He also wants fishing rights in the Dnieper and our niece Lubava in marriage. My lord, summon your men-at-arms and have that monster thrown into the dungeons."

The Prince looked aghast and began clapping his hands.

He clapped and clapped until all the wall hangings started to shake, but not a servant appeared to answer the summons. It looked indeed as though the palace were deserted.

"Do they want to lose their heads then?" cried Vladimir when, to his horror, Khan Udol came into the hall, nodded carelessly, made his way to the Golden Table, and sat down in the Prince's place under the big crimson canopy.

"How dare you sit there, you infidel?" shouted Vladimir, but the Tartar shook his head.

"You would be wise not to start a quarrel, Prince of Kiev," he said in a dangerously calm voice. "I have come here unarmed, but I carry my magic whistle, and its sound carries for twenty-two miles. I have fifty thousand men under arms and as soon as they hear the whistle, they will ride into Kiev." He stopped and laughed. "See, I have waited for all your gallant Knights to be away. I am not afraid of anyone else in your principality. Your soldiers are men of straw and your servants are cowards. I am your guest and I expect you to speak pleasantly to me. I happen to be very hungry."

Husband and wife exchanged anguished glances, but there seemed nothing for them to do except to make for the great vaulted kitchens. They found them deserted. Not a cook, not a scullion but had taken their refuge in the cellars. But the food had been cooked. As usual, there was enough for hundreds of people.

For something like two hours the Prince and his wife fetched and carried for that monster Udol. He emptied a huge tureen of soup at one gulp, asked for another, and another, and yet another. There was no need to cut bread for Udol: a huge loaf meant one bite for him. He ate several roast geese in rapid succession and seven apple pies, each the size of a cart wheel. Then he fell asleep, his enormous feet stretched out.

Princess Anna wept.

"My lord, is this the end of our fair Kiev? When the monster wakes up, he will demand the fishing rights on the Dnieper and Lubava. Poor child, she has gone on a pilgrimage to the nuns at St. Basil's, and I have not even got a messenger to send to her. We seem deserted by everybody. My lord, what are we to do?"

"We will go and say a prayer in the Cathedral," Vladimir answered.

So Anna put a pale blue veil over the tall white *kokoshnik* on her head, and the Prince led her out of the palace. As soon as they were out of the gates, whispers reached them from every half-shuttered window:

"My lord, don't judge us too hard—we dare not come out."

"That hideous Tartar passed here and threatened to whistle for his army if we helped you . . ."

"My lord, what has happened?"

"And what is he doing now?"

"He ate an enormous dinner and he is asleep," Vladimir replied. "Don't worry, my good people. The Knights will soon be back and God will deliver us."

Vladimir and Anna entered St. Sophia's, lit two candles at the shrine of Our Lady of Sudden Joy, prayed fervently, and came out. Suddenly the Princess saw a slim boy walking along the Street of Wisdom.

"My lord, tell him to hide somewhere. Poor lad . . . He must be from the country—how dusty his feet are! I suppose he knows nothing about the danger."

The Prince called. The lad turned and ran up. He wore a tattered smock and his feet were bare, but his face looked distinguished and also serene—just as though he had spent all his years in sunlight. It did the hearts of the Prince and his lady good to look at him.

The boy bowed low and said simply:

"My lord, I am sent here by my father, Ignatius, Knight of the Golden Table. He gave me his blessing and his crimson silk girdle. He thought you might find me useful."

Vladimir looked sad. He had not forgotten Ignatius and he well knew the great virtue of the crimson silk girdle, but he doubted if its power could ever be evoked by a stripling. Still, he spoke kindly:

"Welcome to Kiev, dear son. We greatly honored your father. Is he in better health?"

"My lord, he died a month ago, and he named the day I was to come to you," answered the boy. "But what has happened to Kiev? The gates were open, the watch would not come out, and the streets are empty."

"You should return to your manor, my boy," replied the Prince and told him about Udol.

The boy bowed again and said:

"My lord, I am a Knight's son and it is my custom to respect my father's wishes." He added, "He had me christened Michael because of his great love for the Archangel."

Vladimir shook his head.

"You may come and see for yourself," he said at last, "but I fear there is nothing to be done until the Knights are back."

They entered the great hall, and the Prince ordered Michael to keep near the door. Khan Udol woke up and said it was time for supper. Once again Vladimir and Anna descended into the vast kitchens, the Prince having told Michael not to move from a dark alcove by the door. They brought seven boars' heads, five hams, two huge pigeon pies, twelve loaves of rye bread, and Vladimir staggered up with a barrel of mead. Udol cast a contemptuous look at the food.

"So you think that would do for me?" he growled. "Do you want me to blow my whistle?"

"There is nothing else left in the kitchens," Vladimir told him, and Udol pursed his lips.

"And you call yourself a wealthy prince, do you? Well, it is better than nothing," and he fell on the boars' heads, the hams, the pies and the bread. In less than half an hour the board was cleared. Udol leaned back and bared his sharp yellow teeth in an unpleasant grin.

"I am still hungry, but never mind! I want you to sign the deed about those fishing rights and I want to marry your niece not later than tomorrow morning. Is she in the palace?"

"No," Anna replied.

"Where is she?"

Anna glanced at her husband. He kept silent. So did she.

"Shall I blow my whistle then?"

Vladimir shrugged and said nothing.

Udol unbuttoned his coat and drew out a big silver whistle shaped like a crescent. Anna went pale.

Udol opened his mouth very wide and his cheeks bulged out. He looked more hideous than ever. Very deliberately he put the whistle between his lips.

Nobody had ever heard such an appalling noise. The

goblets, dishes and spoons on the table were all shattered. It sounded far worse than the combined blast of a thousand trumpets. The Princess, swaying on her feet, thought she had gone deaf forever, and she reminded herself that it did not matter so very much because they had less than one hour to live. She turned her head and looked at her husband. Vladimir stood there in his golden coat and high green boots, and seemed as unconcerned as though he were in the company of good friends.

The stillness after that noise was almost equally unbearable. Udol leaned back, leered and said:

"Vladimir, Prince of Kiev, by daybreak tomorrow not a stone will be left on stone in your city."

The Prince said calmly:

"I have tried to rule in honor these many years. May it please God to let me die in honor. You shall not marry my nice, Udol, nor will any rights be granted to you."

"Well, my men will be here in less than ten minutes," Udol told him, and the Cathedral belfry chimed the hour.

They waited. They lost all idea of time. They were startled to hear the belfry chime the half-hour. Udol's face darkened.

"I suppose the wind is against them." He tried to speak carelessly. When Michael moved away from the door towards the middle of the hall, evening sunlight suddenly broke through the latticed windows and turned the boy's grey smock into a gold-embroidered coat. His eyes clear and tranquil, Michael waited for Udol to say something, but the Khan kept silent. Then the boy bowed to Vladimir.

"It is time I served you, my lord. My father said I was

too young to wear armor, but he left me a weapon which had never failed him."

What followed happened so quickly that neither Vladimir nor Anna ever quite remembered later how it was done. At one moment, there was Khan Udol seated in the red-canopied chair, his face full of venom. The next instant, Michael having waved a crimson silk girdle, there was the Khan turned into a puppet, and even his huge feet were the size of a doll's feet. His voice rang so faint that it was difficult for Vladimir to hear it:

"Ignatius's crimson girdle again . . . And I knew he was dead . . . Oh dear, how many men haven't I sent to get hold of that accursed girdle, and not one of them ever came back . . . And what has happened to my fifty thousand men? Surely, surely, they must have heard my whistle . . ."

Nobody answered him. Michael waved the crimson girdle again and again, and the doll in the Khan's clothes stopped muttering and moving, and fell off the red-draped chair, a little bundle of brown cloth and white leather.

Princess Anna staggered towards a chair. Vladimir rubbed his forehead.

"Son," he said to Michael, "I must reward you, but we are not out of danger yet. I can't quite understand it—surely, Udol's army must have heard that horrible whistle."

The boy blushed scarlet.

"My lord, I passed by the Tartar camp before I came to the city. I remembered my father's wishes. There are fifty thousand little dolls lying very still, and they will never get up again."

The Prince went into the great square and shouted the news to his people. All the windows were at once unshuttered and people streamed to give thanks in the Cathedral. The men-at-arms and the household rushed from the cellars, and they looked deeply ashamed of themselves, though the Prince did not reproach them.

The very next day young Michael was given a gold spur.

"I name you Knight of the Golden Table," said Vladimir, but the boy did not kneel to receive the touch of the Prince's sword on his shoulder.

"My lord, my father told me I was not to remain in Kiev. I must look after the manor for two years. There are geese and cows and timber to be seen to."

The Prince looked amazed.

"Surely, there must be someone else on your late father's manor who can look after those matters? Poultry and timber! That is hardly a life for a lad who has proved his knightly virtue!"

"I have not proved it, my lord," replied Michael. "It was my late father's blessing and the power of his crimson girdle. What Knight could I be when my knees shook at the mere sight of Khan Udol?"

Vladimir thought very hard.

"Since such was your late father's wish," he said at last, "I suppose you must return, but I cannot send you back empty-handed. Is there anything you would like?"

Michael lost no time in saying:

"Yes, my lord, I would like a fishing net."

"You shall have the best net to be found in Kiev," Vladimir told him, "and in two years you must return to be a Knight."

So it happened, and two years later, on his return to Kiev, Michael found that the Prince's musicians had composed a ballad in his honor. In the ballad, the wicked Udol's horde had swollen to one hundred thousand and Michael's age was reduced from twelve to seven. So he came to be remembered as the child-deliverer of Kiev from a Tartar invasion.

How Dounai Won a Bride
for Prince Vladimir

How Dounai Won a Bride
for Prince Vladimir

It so happened that Princess Anna died within five years of her wedding day, and Vladimir would not be comforted for a long time. The Golden Table was draped with a fine white cloth in sign of mourning, and the Prince did not wear his jeweled collar. For six months his musicians did not come to the hall, and Vladimir hardly spoke at meals. The Bishop, the nobles, and the Knights did all they could to divert him, but there was so little for them to do. Vladimir could not ride out with his falconers because of mourning, nor could he hunt the bear and the wolf. And, unfortunately, Kiev was passing through a very tranquil time. Nobody threatened Vladimir with an invasion. Even the dragons were quiet, and court soothsayers vied with one another in foretelling a long period of unbroken peace.

At last, they all took counsel together. Their Prince must surely marry again. Princess Anna had borne him one son, but the child had died in infancy, and the succession must be made safe. So they all went to Prince Vladimir and found him watching his favorite white pigeons at their dinner.

Vladimir listened to the men's arguments, shook his head, and said sadly:

"You may be right, but where could I look for another bride? There are no more princesses in Byzantium."

"My lord," they replied, "Byzantium is not the only

country in the world. There are the courts of Denmark, England and Norway, to say nothing of others."

"Very well," Vladimir said wearily, "I'll marry again if such be your wish."

At once orders were issued for the equipment of the bridal embassy, and Kiev stirred into life. Mourning was laid aside. The Prince put on his jewels again, and the white cloth was taken off the Golden Table. In the great market and in the streets strangers stopped one another and said how glad they were their lord was to look for another wife. They had loved Princess Anna very deeply, but the palace without its liege lady was like a winter without snow.

The embassy consisted of a bishop, four monks, twenty nobles, ten Knights and a crowd of servants. The nobles wore scarlet tunics, that color traditionally explaining the purpose of their mission, and the Knights had scarlet plumes on their helmets. Much care was taken to choose what went by the name of the bridal earnest: the first gifts of bridegroom to bride and her nearest kin. Vladimir ordered his treasurer to make a lavish selection, and eighty-five large saddlebags were packed with cups and goblets of pure gold, pieces of velvet and silk, diamonds, topaz, and pearls, finely embroidered veils, and many things cunningly worked in ivory and in amber. The bishop was entrusted with the Prince's betrothal ring, a great square sapphire engraved with a dove. Ilya of Murom carried Vladimir's letters to the King of Denmark.

The embassy left Kiev, and the city started getting ready for the great day of their triumphant return. The cupolas of all the churches were regilded, and new carpets were laid all over the palace. The Prince himself sent two bags of rare pearls for the embellishment of the shrine of Our Lady of Sudden Joy at St. Sophia's. Peasants were told that their tribute of meat and game would have to be doubled for some months to come, and a few new taxes were introduced to replenish the exchequer. But nobody grumbled. They so much wanted to see a princess at the palace again.

Months went by. The embassy returned. They all wore long faces, and the sumptuous saddlebags had not even been unpacked. The King of Denmark had two daughters, three sisters, seven nieces, and more female cousins than he could ever remember, but he had refused to consider the proposal. He had said that he would never feel at peace if he let a woman of his house go to such a turbulent place as Kiev seemed to be.

Presently the embassy left on another journey. In four years they visited many courts and always returned with the same answer. The people of Kiev took to murmuring, and the Knights of the Golden Table urged Vladimir to challenge those proud countries.

"It is a bitter insult to you, my lord," argued Ilya of Murom, and they all echoed his words, but the Prince shook his head.

"It means that it would be better for me not to take another woman to wife. There is Gleb, my nephew, to succeed me."

When the Knights heard that name, they would have stamped their feet if it were not for the Prince's presence. Gleb was about twenty-four, and he was such a coward that he had been known to shake at the sight of a rat scurrying across the floor. He disliked riding. He lived wholly for his stomach. He began eating when he woke up in the morning and he did not stop until he went to bed at night. Nobody could really tell if he were clever or stupid; Gleb considered it very bad manners to talk with his mouth full, and so he never spoke at all.

"Such a prince," they all said to one another, "would be the ruin of Kiev. Justice would be neglected. There would be no voice heard in council, and all the cooks would be overworked and the peasants crushed by increased tribute of meat and game. Why, Gleb might even be capable of surrendering the principality to the Tartars so long as they allowed him to have all his meals in peace."

Naturally, such rumors reached Vladimir in time. One evening at supper he cried:

"Haven't I tried my utmost to find another bride? Well, if you feel like that about my nephew, do something instead of murmuring among yourselves. There may well be a girl of noble birth somewhere captured by a dragon in some remote country. Go and fetch her if you can."

And here the youngest Knight of them all, Dounai, leaped to his feet and said boldly:

"My lord, I heard of one such this very morning, and she is said to be as beautiful as she is good."

Everybody stopped eating the baked sturgeon on their platters. Dounai was a mere stripling, recently knighted for a gallant exploit against the Tartars. What princess could he be talking about? There was not a court left unvisited by Vladimir's embassy.

Dounai went on:

"Yes, my lord, and all of us would be happy to have her as our liege lady."

The Knights stared at him, so young and handsome in a loose crimson coat and white breeches. He stood, his

92

hands pressed against the Golden Table, his lips smiling.

"Why didn't you mention her before?" asked Vladimir. "We might have saved all the expense of those embassies."

"I knew nothing about her, my lord, until this morning."

"Well, you might try and bring this wonderful girl to Kiev. I shall not forget your services. By the way, who is she?"

"Eupraxia, daughter of Duke Jagon of Bielowez."

The Knights dropped their spoons and stared. Even the servants stopped replenishing goblets. Vladimir stroked his beard in silence.

Duke Jagon of Bielowez was lord of an immense forest at a great distance to the west of Kiev. He seemed satisfied with his possessions and never invaded his neighbor's dominions. Nor did he want to make friends with them. Rumor had it that Jagon was a warlock, though nobody had ever met him. Everybody had heard about his pride— Jagon traced his descent back to Adam. Nobody knew even the name of the woman who was his wife, and nobody knew that he had a daughter. The mere idea that Jagon's daughter might become the princess of Kiev was unpleasing.

"What an alliance that would be," said Vladimir at last, and the Knights at once approved of the mockery in his voice. "I believe that Jagon has a city somewhere in the depths of his forest, but I don't think anyone has ever seen it. And where, Dounai, have you learned about the virtues of that wonderful lady? I had no idea of her existence."

"Two pilgrims passed through Kiev yesterday," Dounai replied. "They said they had lost their way, and found themselves at Bielowez, and Jagon would have had them beheaded for the trespass if it had not been for Eupraxia. She gave them food, money, and new smocks, and she led them out of the forest. They told me that the people of Bielowez worship the imprint of her feet. So good is she that even wolves stop snarling when they see her."

"And is she beautiful?"

"So lovely is she that the pilgrims were afraid to look at her too much. They thought the light in her eyes might blind them forever."

"Do you know the way into the forest?"

"No, my lord," Dounai replied modestly.

"Well, you'll have to learn it. Go and fetch that prodigy. See, Dounai, I take you at your word. You will lose your head if you fail to bring her. Go, here is my sapphire ring as a token, and remember, I never wish to see such a father-in-law here at Kiev."

Dounai bowed and went. All the Knights said to one another that they would never see him again. The very few men who had dared go inside Jagon's forest never returned.

For three days and three nights Dounai rode westward. So handsome, young, and courteous he was that everybody in the villages he passed was only too pleased to give him food and to care for his splendid black horse. When they heard that Dounai was on his way to Jagon's fastness, they wept for sorrow that they would never see him again.

On the fourth day Dounai came to a great plain. The forest loomed beyond it. Even at that distance it would have struck fear into anyone's heart, so vast, thick, and dark it was, immense firs all but brushing against the skyline. As Dounai rode on, he saw no birds flying about, nor were there any small beasts scurrying among the tangled undergrowth.

"I am on the Prince's service. I belong to the Fellowship," he said to reassure himself as he reached the outskirts of the forest. Many paths ran ahead, all narrow and twisting, and Dounai did not know where they led. No bird's song was there to hearten him, and for the first time since leaving Kiev, the young man wished that he had kept silent at the Prince's table.

He chose a path at random, and it got more and more twisted as he rode on. Fir branches smote at his head and shoulders, but the black horse did not stumble. Yet the shadows thickened all the time until Dounai could barely see the bridle between his fingers. Then suddenly the horse stopped. Dounai urged him on, but the beast seemed rooted to the ground. And in less than an instant Dounai found himself in absolute darkness. He could not even see the silver bit of his bridle.

Then he heard a woman's soft voice somewhere to the left of him:

"Turn your horse at once and ride back to safety and God's daylight."

"Madam," Dounai replied, "I cannot see you and I do not know who you are, but yours is a friend's advice, and I am grateful. I may indeed find my way back to daylight, but never to safety because a block awaits me if I fail in my mission," and he went on to tell the woman whom he could not see why he had ridden out to Bielowez.

"Your Prince is cruel to send you on such an errand. I am Jagon's wife. He has exiled me from the palace into a hut in the forest because I taught my daughter to be kind to people and animals. My husband says she would have been as cruel as he is if it had not been for me. And he will never let her marry anyone. He would not trust anyone else to cook his food, and I am afraid that she has no great love of the kitchen, poor child."

"Madam," Dounai said with great feeling, "as Princess of Kiev, she need never handle a saucepan."

A pause followed. The Duchess was obviously lost in thought. Dounai waited. The forest was eerily still. You would have thought there was no life in it. And it was dreadfully close. Dounai felt as though he had been plunged into a steamy bath. His forehead and hands were clammy. He breathed with an effort.

At last the Duchess spoke:

"I believe yours is a rich and lovely country, and I would dearly like my daughter to go there. I think there is one way to achieve it, but it is the way of a lie. There is one thing my husband dreads more than any other—and that is to know the forest invaded. Many lone travelers have indeed come here, and they were all captured, and the wolves he keeps at the back of the palace tore them to pieces. So you must tell the Duke that you have come with a great force. Tell him anything else you like. Once he is frightened he is like a snowman under strong spring sunshine. But it must be a convincing lie. Can you, being a Knight, tell such?"

"It will be a lie to a good purpose, Madam," Dounai replied quietly.

"In such a case I can lead you to the gates of his fastness. I can do no more."

There was a rustle as though a heap of dead leaves were being stirred, and Dounai felt a hand seize his bridle. The horse obeyed the touch and moved off. It proved a very long trek across the forest, but the Duchess knew the way. Gradually, the shadows grew thinner and thinner, and Dounai saw her head shawled in grey. She never turned round or spoke. At last they came to a big clearing. At the end of it ran a high wall of dark red stone with a black iron gateway in the middle.

"Here I must leave you," said the lady. Then she let go the bridle, pulled the veil over her head and ran back so fast that she vanished in less time than it would have taken Dounai to eat a cherry.

He rode on. The gateway was ajar, and he pushed it open with a booted foot. For an instant he remained gazing. Jagon's fastness was a miniature city of low dark red houses. The street facing Dounai ended in a square where he saw bears and wolves running about on their hind legs and shouting in human voices that their sanctuary had been violated. Dounai quite expected his mount to get frightened by so many wild beasts at large but the animal kept calm, even when an immense brown bear ran up and screamed:

"However did you find your way in here? Nobody has ever ridden through the forest—"

"But I have," Dounai replied, "because I have business with the Duke."

At these words the bear's right forepaw went up to his forehead and pulled hard. Dounai saw an ugly sallow face of a man.

"What a fancy dress affair," he said pleasantly, "and it is a long time till Carnival, isn't it? Please take me to your master."

The sallow-faced man looked stupefied. Then he

turned and led Dounai to the porch of the palace and through a dim passage into an immense hall, its floor and walls covered with animal skins. Fur rugs covered every chair and trestle. On a dais sat Jagon, dressed in a cloak of fox skins, a great bearskin cap on his head. He was so huge that the top of the cap almost touched the ceiling. On the table before him lay a great ham flanked by a goblet, an inkhorn and a roll of parchment. When Dounai entered, Jagon seized the inkhorn in mistake for the goblet, and the taste of ink by no means improved his temper. He roared:

"A stranger? Well, my wolves are hungry enough. But you should have been seized in the forest. How dare you break my sanctuary?"

"Envoys on a peaceful mission," said Dounai, "cannot break sanctuary, Duke Jagon. They should be received with honor."

"I'll leave it to my pet wolves to pay you honor," Jagon thundered, and Dounai shook his head.

"May I ask how many wolves there are, Duke Jagon?"

"There were fifteen, but one fell into a mantrap in the forest."

"Fourteen wolves?" Dounai reflected. "What is that number against three thousand men."

Duke Jagon seized the ham and broke the knuckle in two.

"Three thousand men?" he echoed hoarsely, "and you stand there and tell me you have come on a peaceful mission! Let me but blow my trumpet, and thirty thousand of my men will cross the forest and offer battle," and Jagon blew a brass trumpet so loudly that all the wall hangings shook for several minutes.

The summons was answered none too hurriedly by the sallow-faced man.

"Muster the bodyguard and the army," thundered Jagon. "The country is in danger. Well, what are you waiting for?"

"Sir," the man mumbled, "fifty men are hunting the bear and fifty men are after the wolf, and fifty men have gone fishing according to your orders. I have fifty men in the city—but those are all furriers, and it is their day off, sir. However, is it your pleasure that I order them to cross the forest?"

"Hold your tongue," Jagon roared. "How often have I told you never to speak the truth? Get all the furriers in and tell them to take this man to the back of this palace, do you hear?"

"Sir," the unhappy man answered, "as you know well, the furriers are terrified of the wolves. We must wait for the return of the men gone after the wolf in the forest."

"Wait?" Jagon raised both arms above his head, "With three thousand men waiting to cross the forest? If I had anyone else in the household, I would kill you this very instant!"

Dounai took a step forward.

"Duke Jagon," he said, courteously. "You have not even asked me about my mission. Prince Vladimir has sent me here with a sapphire ring for your daughter."

"You bring three thousand men and you want to steal my Eupraxia," shouted Jagon, "and you call yours a peaceful mission! Have I ever invaded anyone's dominions? Have I ever interfered with anyone's business? Tell your Prince that I'll never allow her to marry. Who would grill my sausages, cure hams and make puddings once she is gone from Bielowez?"

"Indeed, there is no one at all to cook for my master," the sallow-faced man said mournfully. "Once I tried to cook a couple of eggs for him, and I kept them in boiling water for hours, but the shells never softened."

Dounai said nothing. But he could not help wondering how long it would be before Duke Jagon discovered that no single man-at-arms from Kiev was outside the forest. The fifty men who were then hunting the bear and the fifty men who were after a wolf would presumaby return before sunset. Dounai thought about the wolves at the back of the palace, and knew he did not relish such an end.

"But I can't draw back now," he thought, and at that very moment Eupraxia came in. She wore a white cloak and a shimmering blue veil on her head, and so beautiful she was that Dounai hardly dared look at her. He unhelmed himself and went down on one knee.

"This fellow," sneered Jagon, "has brought a sapphire ring for you from Prince Vladimir of Kiev—"

"He is not a fellow," replied Eupraxia, "but a Knight of the Golden Table, and we should be honored by such a visit."

"Eupraxia," roared the affectionate father. "I would kill you if you were not such a good cook! What do you mean by coming here? You should be in the kitchen seeing to my supper."

"Your supper," Eupraxia told him, "is ready, and I have left all my recipe books on the kitchen table. Have one of your furriers taught to cook, and you will lack for nothing, not even for that spiced cranberry sauce you have for the roast goose. I have had a message, Father, and I am leaving you. There will be much for me to do in Kiev."

"Who could have sent you any such message?" cried Jagon and struck his fist on the table so hard that two of its legs were splintered.

"The Knight in command of three thousand men outside the forest. They will escort me to Prince Vladimir," Eupraxia answered proudly, and Dounai raised his head and gazed at her in wonder. He could not understand. Had the Princess met her mother? Was it witchery?

But there was not much time for reflection. He stretched out his right hand, and Eupraxia stooped and took the sapphire ring. On seeing it, Jagon swore a terrible oath and then broke into tears. But Eupraxia, followed by Dounai, was by the door. There was nobody to stop them. Outside, the fifty furriers had all gone indoors, and Dounai, Eupraxia riding pillion, went as fast as he could through the terrible forest. And there stood a mighty host sent from Kiev to escort Vladimir's bride. Dobryna told Dounai:

"The Prince was determined that you should not fail."

All along the way people in the villages wept for joy to see the handsome young Knight return safely to Kiev.

But Dounai's heart was as heavy as lead. He knew that he had seen the most beautiful face in the world. His heart was given to his master's chosen bride. He brought her to Kiev and to Vladimir's palace, and then rode away without waiting for his reward. He crossed the Dnieper by a ford and rode westwards till he came to the banks of another wide river as yet unchristened, and he asked its clear blue waters to receive his sorrow together with his body. He could not marry Eupraxia and he could not live without her. He jumped into the river and on that day, as is told in many ancient stories, the great river received its name—which was also his own, but the countries in the west call it the Danube.

Vassily and Curly Head the Brigand

THE SEVENTH TALE

Vassily and Curly Head
the Brigand

For three years, three months and three days Kiev had enjoyed unbroken peace. The watch on the red-roofed turrets almost forgot how to use their trumpets to sound alarm in the city. There were no pirates prowling up and down the Dnieper, and green and blue silks from Byzantium, fawn gloves from Novgorod, and amber necklaces from the Baltic shore were sold in the market place. Vladimir and Eupraxia were busily superintending the building of yet another blue- and gold-roofed hall in their palace. But the Knights of the Golden Table were getting rather restless. All the witches were dead and there were hardly any dragons to speak of. The Knights held daily mock combats in the palace yard, but that was hardly an occupation to satisfy them. One morning Ilya of Murom went to see Vladimir.

"My dear lord," said Ilya, "we ask your leave to go on a pilgrimage to Byzantium. We would like to pray for your health at St. Sophia's. We'll return with many precious icons for your chapel and a bolt of purple velvet for your lady."

Vladimir at once summoned his soothsayers. They spent a whole night in studying the stars, and they told the Prince that the future promised well. Next morning all the Knights, led by Ilya of Murom, embarked for Byzantium in scarlet painted barges, each with a big gilded lion carved at the prow.

Within ten days the watchmen had to blow their trumpets. The plain to the southwest of the city was dotted with white tents erected in one night. They were shaped like onions and flaunted red triangular banners.

Kiev was thrown into confusion. Were they Tartars, or Khozars, or some unknown savage tribe from the south? Nobody knew, and Vladimir was so troubled that he forgot to order the beheading of the soothsayers who had misled him.

There were some foot soldiers in Kiev, and the Prince's men-at-arms were skilful enough with the pike and the axe, but there were so few of them and none possessed the great virtue of the Knights.

Vladimir sent out some scouts. They reported that it was the horde of Curly Head, a terrible brigand come all the way from the deep south to plunder Kiev, and that the force was some forty odd thousand strong. "Curly Head must have sacked many cities already," they told the Prince. "The tents are furnished with rare hangings, there are jugs of silver and gold and tables of ivory."

Hot on the heels of the Kievan scouts came a herald from Curly Head. The Kievans stared at the man with amazement. He wore a crimson mantle striped with green and edged with rare fur, white boots with green stone buttons, and a scarf of gold brocade. He rode a magnificent grey, caparisoned in blue velvet. He brought a message embroidered in small pearls on a piece of red velvet; it was Curly Head's challenge to Vladimir to meet him in open combat.

Princess Eupraxia at once said:

"You, my lord, are an anointed sovereign, and you cannot possibly fight a common brigand. The men-at-arms must be sent out to punish him as he deserves."

But Vladimir said sadly:

"My men-at-arms are just one hundred strong, and they are ordinary men—they are not like the Knights."

"It is all my fault," Eupraxia wept, her head on his shoulder. "I urged you to let them go to Byzantium—I wanted that purple velvet so much!"

"Please," the Prince said, "I wish you would not distress yourself so. We are not quite undone. The nobles and the merchants will help me."

"What help is there to expect from them?" asked Eupraxia. "The merchants always fall on their feet even when a city is sacked. And the nobles will merely ride away to their manors. No, my lord, I should call on artisans and peasants. Give them plenty to eat and drink, and I am sure they will find a way. Heavens," the Princess went on, "when I think of all the victories you have won, I will not believe that a common bandit can do us much harm."

"My dear," Vladimir sighed, "that common bandit has more than forty thousand men under him."

Curly Head's herald rode away without a definite answer from the Prince, and the palace kitchens got very busy. Broiling and boiling, roasting and baking went on all through the night. Large trestles were set up and down the great square. Crowds of artisans and peasants ate and drank at their Prince's expense, but when Vladimir spoke to them of the danger, they all hung their heads and had nothing to say. They finished the mead in their goblets and went away, except for one elderly man who followed

the Prince into the palace yard and said very softly:

"The Knights are indeed away, but, lord, there is Vassily."

Vladimir frowned.

"No, I had to have him expelled from the Fellowship, he gambled so violently—even down to his helmet. I heard he had gone to Chernigov. I would not have him stay here."

"Lord, did you send him into exile?"

"No. His expulsion was punishment enough."

"Vassily is back in Kiev, lord," said the elderly man. "I keep the Grey Falcon, and he is there. It is true that he has gambled everything away—even the shield blessed by the Bishop."

"The scoundrel," cried Vladimir hotly. "How could I ever ask him for help? There can be no knightly virtue left in such a man! Dice mean far more to him than his oath! Vassily could not fight forty geese, let alone forty thousand men!"

But the host of the Grey Falcon shook his head.

"My lord," he said weightily, "knightly virtue may sometimes fall asleep but it can never be lost altogether."

Yet the Prince would not agree. He went back to the palace and told the Princess that he would never have Vassily back in his service. Eupraxia was too wise to argue with her husband. She went to her rooms, summoned her ladies, told them to put some of her choicest pearls into a small bag, then covered her head and shoulders with a thick veil, and secretly went to the Grey Falcon.

Vassily was in the back room. He lay on a trestle, a large piece of sacking over him, and she told him what she wanted him to do.

"For me to meet Curly Head?" he said, his eyes wide with wonder. "Lady, I am a lost man. I possess neither horse nor armor. Why, I have gambled away my shield blessed by the Bishop."

Eupraxia stamped her foot.

"I have brought enough to redeem all," she said impatiently, "and here," she held up a tiny bag of white silk, "is something to make that brigand go to sleep. Remember, the powder would not work for anyone except a Knight. Hide it well—I leave the opportunity to you. You must contrive it, but time is running short."

"I will go and meet Curly Head," Vassily said at last. "I could not disregard the Prince's wishes. Lady, you did say you were here at his pleasure?"

"Certainly," Eupraxia replied hurriedly and went as secretly as she had come.

Vassily got ready. He put on his armor, they saddled the horse for him, and he rode out of the city and made straight for the camp of Curly Head.

"Friend or foe?" the sentry challenged him, and Vassily laughed.

"Don't you recognize me? I am Vassily, once of the Fellowship of the Golden Table. Could I be friends with a prince who has expelled me with such ignominy? Lead me to Curly Head. I have business with him, and I am very hungry and thirsty."

The sentry at once called a soldier who led Vassily to a large tent where Curly Head, a slim and wiry man with shifty pale eyes and very long moustaches, sat finishing his supper. He wore a coat of amethyst velvet and green silk breeches. He was eating off gold and the table was of ivory inlaid with mother-of-pearl. Vassily cast a glance about the tent and saw there were enough riches in it to pay the ransom of twelve Knights.

Curly Head looked up and bared his teeth in a grin:

"You come from Kiev? They were not very civil to my herald. I suppose Vladimir is afraid to meet me in open combat?"

Vassily shook his head.

"I do not know. I have not seen the Prince, Curly Head. I have ridden here to tell you that all the Knights are away and that the city of Kiev is yours for the taking. Why, man, you have the chance of a lifetime. You could have this tent paved with diamonds."

Curly Head did not seem impressed.

"It sounds too good to be true, but is it true? Even if all the Knights were away, the people are there, and Vladimir's men-at-arms, too—"

"Vladimir's men-at-arms are so many mouse-hearted men," retorted Vassily, "and there are no people left in Kiev. They all died of fright as soon as they heard the alarm trumpets. I tell you the gates will stand wide open. You will be able to plunder at your pleasure, and I'll show you the houses of the wealthiest merchants."

Curly Head stroked his moustaches.

"You do hate Vladimir," he remarked at last, and Vassily's face flushed darkly.

"Wouldn't you if you were in my place?"

"Well, then, I'd better muster my men and lead them at once."

But Vassily shook his head.

"No, Curly Head. Were you to bring the whole horde into Kiev, they'd sack it and there might not be much left for yourself. If I were you, I would ride in with a bodyguard of, say, fifty picked men. I'll come with you and I know where you can find plenty of padlocks. You'll have the best treasures locked up in safety. Then have the horde in. Let them make for the inns."

"Vladimir was indeed a fool to dismiss you," said the bandit. "You have got a head on your shoulders. Yes, I'll take fifty of my best men. I'll go and speak to the captain of the bodyguard and tell the servants to set out fifty-one stirrup cups. No, it must be fifty-two."

"This will do for my stirrup cup," replied Vassily and emptied a goblet from the table. He hoped his hand was not shaking. He had never expected such a chance to fall into his lap.

"Well," said Curly Head, "I warn you—I may be quite a time. I must see my hairdresser and the master of the wardrobe. I could not ride into Kiev in this shabby old coat and with all my curls untidy and unscented."

"Thank you, Curly Head," Vassily replied, his heart beating wildly, "I will have some more of your excellent wine."

Curly Head went off to see the captain, the hairdresser and the master of the wardrobe. Presently servants came in with fifty-one cups filled with choicest wine, set them on a long trestle, and were about to withdraw when Vassily asked caselessly:

"How long do you think your master will take to get ready?"

"The hairdresser never hurries," answered one of the servants. "The master may well take over an hour."

"Then," Vassily announced, "I am going to rest. I have had a very hard day of it. Please call me when the master is about to come."

The servants said they would and withdrew.

Vassily had a little more wine. Then he got out the little white bag given him by the Princess, untied the thongs, and sniffed. The smell reassured him: it was the petals of the blue poppy—known as the slumber flower. Very carefully he moved toward the trestle and listened—but there was not a sound: Curly Head's servants had more sense than dare to disturb their master's guest.

Vassily dropped a pinch of pale powder into each of the fifty-one goblets. Then he carefully hid the bag out of sight and stretched himself on red velvet cushions. It was quite an hour before Curly Head appeared, his hair most elaborately waved and perfumed. He wore a splendid coat of gold brocade, green velvet breeches, and beautiful fawn boots with emerald buttons.

"Curly Head," said Vassily, "you look splendid."

"Do you really think so? Well, I did not wish to ride in shabby clothes. The men have their horses saddled. They'd better come in for their stirrup cups," and Curly Head clapped his hands.

Fifty men came into the tent, and they all looked most ordinary brigands for all the fine clothes they wore. They stood by the trestle, each holding his goblet.

"Good luck to our venture and fifty diamond buckles to each of you, my friends," laughed Curly Head. "Luck is indeed with us. Here is Vassily, who hates Prince Vladimir even more than I do. Drink to him and to our good fortune."

The men cheered wildly and raised the goblets to their lips. Within an instant they were all down on the ground, and Vassily knew well that they would not awake for several hours.

He drew the sword out of its scabbard, cut off Curly Head's head, and hid it in a sack. Then he slipped out of the tent and told the grooms that Curly Head had decided not to ride out until the morning.

"He has asked me to ride ahead and get everything ready for his arrival," he added, and the men accepted all of it since they had heard from Curly Head and the captain of the bodyguard that Vassily was Vladimir's deadly enemy.

Presently Vassily came to the gates of Kiev and told the watch that he wanted twenty-five trumpeters to ride out with him within an hour.

"Those are the Prince's orders," he added.

The watch hesitated.

"We have had no such orders, sir. We must send a messenger to the palace."

"How dare you doubt a Knight's word?" shouted Vassily. "Have you forgotten the manner of our service?" He bent down from the saddle, untied the sack, and set the brigand's head upon his pike. The watch drew back in horror.

"Send someone to the palace at dawn," Vassily went on. "There is no need to disturb the Prince in his sleep. The peril is over. I have put Curly Head to death and here is his head."

Before daybreak Vassily was riding toward the brigand's camp, the red- and blue-coated trumpeters immediately behind him. At Vassily's signal they blew their trumpets, and the whole camp came to life. At the first sight of their leader's head on a pike, they all fled, and Vassily did not pursue them. He rode back to Kiev.

All the bells were ringing and crowds filled streets and

squares, but in the forecourt of the palace Vladimir waited, his eyes full of cold anger.

"You never killed Curly Head in fair fight, did you?" he asked Vassily.

"No, my lord."

"So you have forgotten the covenant of the Fellowship?"

Vassily hung his head.

"Yes," the Prince went on, "my fair city may indeed be delivered from danger—at the price of treachery. How can I live down such shame?"

Vassily kept silent.

"I shall keep you in a dungeon," Vladimir went on, "and wait for your peers' return. Let them pass judgement on you. I did expel you from their company but I never released you from your oath, and you have broken it."

Princess Eupraxia laid her hand on her husband's arm.

"My lord, don't you hear the bells? The enemy is gone. Is this a day to send our deliverer into the dungeons? We are safe."

"At the cost of a shabby trick," her husband replied. "No, my lady, the order stands."

There was no banquet given at the palace that day, and Vassily, his sword and shield taken away from him, was led into one of the deepest dungeons, there to wait for his trial.

When the Knights were back from their pilgrimage and heard the story, they greatly disliked the task imposed on them by Vladimir. It had never happened before. They all hoped it would never happen again. They gathered in the great hall, their faces somber.

Vassily at once admitted he had killed Curly Head by a

trick. The Knights heard him, their eyes lowered.

"Who gave you that powder? Did you purchase it from some sorcerer in the city?" asked Ilya of Murom.

"I never purchased it."

"Who gave it to you?"

"I cannot tell."

"You understand that our judgment will depend on you telling us who gave you the powder?" asked Dobryna.

"I do understand. I cannot tell."

"You were at the Grey Falcon when you first heard about Curly Head?" asked Aliosha.

"And all your armor and your mount were in pawn?"

"They were indeed."

"And everything was redeemed?"

"Yes."

"By whom?" asked Ilya of Murom. "You had no means of your own, had you?"

"No."

"Then who redeemed your gear and your horse?"

"I cannot tell you," said Vassily in a firm clear voice, and the Knights bent their heads again.

"In such a case," said Ilya with a deep sigh, "we must pass judgment of death on you for having broken the oath."

Vassily raised his head.

"I am ready to die," he said loudly, when the door opened and Princess Eupraxia stood there.

"Is the trial over?" she cried in her ringing voice. All the Knights rose, and Ilya answered:

"Yes, my lady. He will not answer our questions. We asked who it was who had given him the powder and redeemed his armor."

"And you have sentenced him to death?"

"We had no other choice, my lady—"

"You are to revoke your judgment," cried Eupraxia. "He has vindicated his Knight's honor. I gave him the powder. I redeemed his armor. If anyone is to suffer, it must be me. Pass your judgment on me," she ended proudly.

"My lady," Ilya of Murom said hurriedly, "we do revoke the sentence. It is not for us to pass judgment on our Prince's lady—"

"Nor is it for me to do so," Vladimir's voice came from the doorway. "Vassily, I re-admit you into the Fellowship."

And within an hour the hall of judgment became the hall of a great feast.

Souchmant's Trial and Triumph

Souchmant's Trial and Triumph

It so happened that Vladimir's Knights started a great argument as to what service would best please their lord. There were always his enemies to fight and to kill, brigands to destroy, dragons and witches to render powerless to do harm. The Knights could not agree among themselves, and they argued so heatedly and loudly that their voices all but drowned the Cathedral bells. Common folk heard the noise and grew uneasy. The peace and prosperity of Kiev were wholly dependent on the Knights' valor. They had never been known to quarrel among themselves, and there they were shouting, gauntleted hands clutching at the swords.

Then suddenly a young man was heard to say:

"Kiev is at peace now. I believe the Prince would be best pleased with a white swan captured without a single arrow striking it, a swan to become a companion to him and his lady."

The Knights burst out laughing.

"Indeed," said Dobryna, "we have often wondered why the Prince should have knighted you, Souchmant. Was it for bringing him an unwounded mouse out of the trap?" And so loudly did they all laugh that the common folk of Kiev were heartened.

Dobryna's gibe was both unkind and untrue. Souchmant was young indeed, but he had won his golden spur in an honorable manner after a single-handed combat with a

Tartar knight far to the south of Kiev. The Tartar, fully armored, was a master at spear throwing. Souchmant, then a peasant, had nothing but a small hatchet, but he bested the Tartar after the second round.

Now blood rushed into Souchmant's face. In his anger he looked more handsome than ever, but he ruled himself so that he spoke calmly:

"What about asking our lord's pleasure?"

They shook their heads. Aliosha said:

"Souchmant, you are a country-bred lad, and you should know that no swan can ever be captured like that."

"It is difficult," Souchmant admitted, "that is why I think the Prince would be pleased."

"Well," Ilya of Murom told him, "the Prince might well decide to send you on such an errand. Be it on your own head!"

Here the loud clang of the noon bell was heard overhead. The Knights at once made for a corner in the great forecourt to get themselves ready for the banquet. Servants brought them water in silver ewers, red-embroidered towels, and fine ivory combs. Each Knight washed his hands and face, combed his hair and beard, and unstrapped his sword belt before entering the hall of the Golden Table. Souchmant, being the youngest, had to await his turn. He was the last to come in, and from the doorway he heard Ilya's deep voice:

"Such is Souchmant's idea, my lord, though we think that it would be easier to climb into the sky than to capture a swan alive and unhurt."

Souchmant's place was farthest from the Prince's crimson-draped chair and he had barely reached it when Vladimir's voice rang loudly:

"Souchmant, I did not knight you to turn you into an idle braggart."

The young man stood very still, his face as white as his shirt.

"Be it on your own head," the Prince went on, "and I give you a week to carry out your idea. A swan, mind you, not a cygnet, and not a feather pulled out."

Souchmant had no dinner that day. He bowed from the hips and left the hall. He went to his lodgings and took a small axe and a sharp-bladed knife. He did not trouble to put on his armor. He rode away from Kiev in a white shirt and loose blue breeches, his head bare, and a great leather bag tied to his silver-embroidered saddle.

He made for the west, for the banks of the Nieprad, known for their herons and swans. But when Souchmant rode near, he could not see a single bird, there was not even a common duck splashing among the reeds, and the Nieprad, famous for its silver-clear waters, was running all turgid and muddy. Souchmant dismounted and decided to make use of an ancient custom taught him by his grandfather. If you knelt by any running water, cupped both hands and drank very slowly, with the blessing on the water in your thought, you could be certain of hearing an answer to any question.

"What has troubled your clear waters, Nieprad?" whispered Souchmant and waited, kneeling, his head bent.

The Nieprad replied:

"My waters are troubled because I am in trouble. I have run here since history began, and I defend Kiev, so deep I run and so treacherous is my drift. Nowhere am I fordable, and often enough I would ask the Lord of the Winds to come to my help when enemy barges tried to cross me. But now—just beyond my north bank, in that great plain dipping down to the horizon, there stands a dreadful host of twenty thousand Tartars come to sack my dear Kiev. For twenty-three days they have tried to build bridges across my breast. For twenty-three nights I have destroyed those bridges. Now I can do no more—and I have been told by the Lord of All Things to wait for a Knight of the Golden Table, and yet time is running short, and not one of them has come." The Nieprad added sadly, "You seem a good man, but you are a peasant and I could not use you for that service."

"I am a Knight of the Golden Table," replied Souchmant, "and I am on the Prince's service. What do you wish me to do?"

"Swim across me," whispered the river. "Do not be anxious—I shall carry you safely. Measure fifty strides from the north bank. An oak stands there. Tear it up by the roots, gather up all its twigs and leaves, and power shall be given you to break the enemy."

Souchmant leaped into the river and swam across in spite of the swift current. There, at a distance of fifty strides, stood the oak, and for a moment the Knight stood still. How could he possibly tear such a giant up by the roots? Yet he knew he must not draw back.

"Am I a Knight for nothing?" he asked himself, stretched out his arms, and encircled the gnarled old trunk. Almost at once the oak swayed right, swayed left, and then fell to the ground, its old roots bared. Souchmant made a big mound of all the little twigs and leaves. The wind dropped, not a leaf stirred, and minute by minute Souchmant felt great power rising in him until he felt that he could have brought down one hundred oaks. At that moment he raised his head and far away toward the horizon he saw the Tartar host make toward him. They were riding shaggy little horses, their crescent-shaped axes glinted in the sunlight, and the red feathers in their caps looked like blood. At that very instant the wind from the Nieprad sang to Souchmant:

"Stay where you are. Stoop for the twigs and the leaves, and throw handfuls of them at the enemy. I'll see that your aim is true."

Souchmant obeyed. Whenever a twig or a leaf touched a Tartar, he at once threw up his arms and fell dead off his horse. But the time came for Souchmant to throw the last handful, and there were not enough twigs or leaves for all the Tartars who were still alive. Two were left. They reined in their horses, took their terrible bows, and aimed at Souchmant.

"Back to the river bank," sang the wind.

Souchment never remembered swimming back. He scrambled up the south bank, one Tartar arrow in his left shoulder and another deep in his right thigh. Then he turned and saw both Tartars jump into the river.

"See to your wounds, dear friend," said the Nieprad, "and I will make the enemy pay dear for the blood you have shed," and in a moment the Tartars were sent to their death by the merciless current.

Souchmant tore bent grass by large handfuls, staunched the blood, and packed blackthorn leaves into the wounds. Then he flung back his head and laughed.

"The Prince will be astonished when he hears of this exploit. I promised to bring him a swan without a single hurt on her body, and I had forgotten all about it. Of course, he'll be far better pleased with this service of mine."

The Nieprad heard and rippled uneasily.

"You should have told me before, but I am afraid there are no swans near here. They all flew far away, the Tartars' shouts having scared them. But I am afraid Prince Vladimir might not believe you. He will want his swan. It would be better for you not to ride back to Kiev."

Souchmant bowed low.

"Queen Nieprad, I am grateful for your kindness, and may your waters soon run clear again, but I would shame my Knight's oath indeed if I did not return to Kiev."

"I knew you would say that," replied the river, "but I had to warn you of the danger."

So Souchmant rode back to Kiev, dried blood on his white shirt and his blue breeches. Some of the Knights met him in the forecourt of the palace and they smiled.

"So the swan must have bested you!"

Souchmant, his wounds beginning to trouble him, made no reply. In the red and blue painted porch he saw Vladimir, who asked:

"Back so soon? And where is my swan?"

"Lord, I have brought you no swan," answered Souchmant. "I met a Tartar host on the north bank of the Nieprad. They were twenty thousand strong, and all are dead. I am sorry, but I have forgotten all about the swan."

"Twenty thousand? What a fable! And you have not even got your shield and sword with you. How could you imagine that such a wild story would serve for an excuse?"

"Send some of the Knights to the Nieprad, my lord," Souchmant answered proudly, "if you need a proof for my words."

"I am sending you to prison," retorted Vladimir. "A Tartar host indeed! Why, my scouts would have brought word to Kiev. Yes, Souchmant, you are going to prison for failing in your service and for the lie you have told me."

The men-at-arms came up and led Souchmant away down a steep dank stair, and they left him in a place where no daylight ever came. They barred and padlocked the heavy iron door, and Souchmant was alone to wait for the Prince's decision on his fate.

Meanwhile, the dinner hour came, and Vladimir was just about to eat his broiled carp when Eupraxia said to him:

"My lord, look at the old pilgrim in the doorway. Why will he not come and ask for his dinner? Perhaps he does not know our customs—"

Vladimir raised his head and saw a tall white-haired pilgrim in a grey smock marked with a big red cross. He stood leaning on his crooked staff and his head was bent as though he were at prayer. The Prince told a servant to invite the old man to have his dinner at one of the tables. But the servant soon returned and said:

"My lord, he says he may not break bread in a house of injustice."

Some among the Knights leaped to their feet, but Vladimir told them to remain seated, and he said to the servant:

"I am lord and judge of Kiev. Tell the pilgrim to come forward and tell me about his case, and I shall give him judgment as the Lord in Heaven directs me."

Presently the old man came near the Golden Table, and Vladimir asked him courteously:

"Do you come from the north, my good man, from the holy places on Lake Ladoga, and have you had any injustice dealt to you within my dominions?"

"I come from the south," replied the pilgrim, "and no

injustice has been dealt to me, but I passed by a river and I crossed a plain where twenty thousand Tartars lie slain."

The Prince frowned.

"I respect your pilgrim's dress, but do you happen to be a kinsman of one called Souchmant? If so, take care. I have already heard the story from him, and I know that he has shamed his Knight's oath by a lie."

"I do not even know the man's name," the old man answered, "though I heard about his great feat from the river where I knelt and drank out of my cupped hands, and later I saw the Tartars lying dead in the great plain, and I was commanded to turn to Kiev and to tell you all I had seen."

Vladimir said nothing, and all went very still in the hall so that a wooden spoon dropped by a careless servant startled everybody, and the Prince stirred.

"Bring me my green boots with gold spurs and have my black horse saddled at once," he ordered. "No, I do not need any armor. I shall ride to the Nieprad, no knight following me."

"Dear husband!" Eupraxia's lips went ashen. "I implore you not to leave Kiev alone. This may well be a trap."

Vladimir shook his head.

"The word 'injustice' has been spoken under this roof, and it is my duty to prove it or disprove it," and, the meal unfinished, he left the hall.

Kiev had an anxious night and an anxious day. In the palace, the princess could not settle down to her needlework, and even her prayers brought her no comfort. All the Knights had their gear and mounts in readiness in case they were summoned to the Prince's rescue. Someone reported the old pilgrim was at prayer in the palace chapel. The dinner bell was not rung that day.

The sun was setting when Vladimir rode back into Kiev. His golden coat looked dusty, his face was grave, and his eyes were red-rimmed as though he had been crying. He hardly answered his people's cheers, and he never waited for the groom to hold his stirrup but leaped out of the saddle and ran across the great forecourt straight toward the door leading into the dungeons.

In a few minutes the whole household and the Knights wondered if they were awake or asleep; never before had they seen their lord kneel before a Knight.

"I ask your pardon, Souchmant," rang Vladimir's deep voice, "for having cast such a slur on your knightly honor."

"My lord," Souchmant stammered, "I beg you will not say such things, and I am still in your debt. There is the swan I must fetch—if I can."

But Vladimir said:

"No service you are likely to render me will ever surpass what you have done," and he took off two sapphire rings given him by the Emperors of Byzantium, put them on the forefinger of Souchmant's right hand, kissed him on the forehead and on both cheeks, and led him into the hall.

Nobody having had any dinner that day, they all enjoyed their supper, none more so than the Knights, their pride in Souchmant's exploit mingled with shame at their earlier contempt of him.

Volkh's Journey to the East

THE NINTH TALE

Volkh's Journey
to the East

ABOUT two miles to the east of Kiev in a small timbered house by the shore of a lake lived a widowed gentlewoman called Martha and her only son, Volkh.

Martha was poor, and she could not afford to buy any of those things which were enjoyed by boys of Volkh's age—green leather boots, coats of scarlet cloth, a sable cap, a horse, and a really good bow. Volkh ran about barefoot, he wore rough smocks in the summer and sheepskins in the winter, had a bow made of withies, and rode a shaggy little pony which was as stubborn as a donkey.

Volkh did not know that his mother had a rare jewel hidden away in the chest in the back room of the house. It was an emerald buckle given to Martha on her wedding day by her godmother, a wise old woman.

"There is great virtue in the buckle," she had said then. "It is neither for wearing nor for selling. Keep it hidden until the day when someone asks for it, and it will cost you dear to part with it, but you must do so."

"How can anyone ask for it when nobody will ever know I have got it, and why should I have to give it up?" Martha had asked, but the old woman would not tell her, and soon after she died.

Now Volkh, who could not remember his father, grumbled often enough about the poor way they lived. He longed for a smart scarlet coat and for a bow made of good Norwegian yew. He grumbled about the wooden trenchers and cups they used at table. He sometimes longed for roast goose and sturgeon for dinner, and Martha could not always afford enough honey for the porridge. And many a time she secretly wished that she might take the emerald buckle to Kiev, sell it to some foreign merchant, and come home, laden with many things for her son's enjoyment, but she dared not break her godmother's wish.

So Volkh passed his twelfth birthday. He had good skill with his bow and, being of noble birth, he could be sent to Kiev to join the Prince's household, but Martha knew she could never afford to equip him for such service. She did not quite know what future awaited him, and she tried not to worry too much. In spite of all his frequent bouts of discontent, Volkh was a good son, and on many occasions Martha was proud of his courage. Volkh was not afraid to wander off into the neighboring woods, and he always came back with something for the larder in his pouch, and he was very clever with his fishing rods.

One summer morning Martha was combing her hair by the window when she heard a great noise outside the gate. Her first thought was that Volkh, who had gone out at dawn, had been killed by a bear. Martha hid her hair under a linen coif and ran down the carved wooden stairway as fast as her trembling legs would carry her.

At once, she breathed in deep relief. Her son stood there, his wet smock gloving his body, his hair, legs and arms all covered with weeds, and by the side of him was an elderly man, dripping from head to foot, his pilgrim's cloak torn and muddy. There was a small crowd behind them, all shouting and clapping. The old pilgrim had fallen into the lake and Volkh had jumped in and pulled him out.

When things were somewhat quieter, Martha told her

maid to get some dry clothing and to set the table for a meal. She offered broiled fish and a rye loaf with apologies for such a scant breakfast, but the old pilgrim said courteously:

"Madam, I am not used to rich fare."

When they had eaten, Volkh ran away to look for the fishing rod he had mislaid, and the pilgrim said:

"Madam, you are known to me though I am a stranger to you. When I was in Jerusalem I had a command given me to come and see you on my return to Rus."

"Who gave it to you?" Martha asked quickly, but the old man did not answer the question and went on:

"You had an emerald buckle given to you on your wedding day and I am here to ask for it."

Martha said sadly:

"This is a very poor manor, and I had always hoped that nobody would come for the buckle while I was alive so that my son might have something for his future," and she sighed, tears welling up in her eyes.

"Your son will never lack anything," the pilgrim said gently, but Martha shook her head. She thought that the old man would probably offer the buckle at some shrine along his way. It certainly seemed unfair, but there was nothing to be done. She got up and went into the back room and returned, a small lime-wood box in her hands.

"I'd much rather not look at it again." Martha laid the box on the table. "May God's blessing be your companion all along the way."

The pilgrim bowed and hid the box in the folds of his smock. Martha did not watch him leave the room; her eyes were all misted with tears. She just did not know what she could do about Volkh's future. She never knew how long she had sat by the table when his excited voice roused her.

"Mother! Mother! Look! I have found it all by the lake shore and everything fits me."

Martha raised her head and remained gazing. Volkh stood there, a magnificent hauberk of Damascene mesh mail on him. He wore beautiful white linen breeches and green boots with silver tassels. There was a bright red plume on his helmet, and his hands, gloved in stout buff leather, held a short pike and an axe.

"Son," Martha gasped at last. "Am I awake or asleep? You look like a Knight of the Golden Table!"

"No, Mother, because there was no shield among the things," Volkh replied.

"But who gave you these wonderful things?"

"The pilgrim. I saw him leave the house, make for the lake shore, and stand there some time, and then I saw the things appear one by one—so quickly, too, it seemed as though they came either from the air or from the ground. I ran as fast as I could. I thought it was all a dream. He waved his hand, said they were all for me, and vanished. Here is a piece of writing."

Neither Martha nor Volkh knew their letters. They took the small piece of parchment to the parish clerk who read out:

"Six wishes for Volkh. Three wishes for Prince Danilo. There is no tenth wish."

"Why, that means I must ride to Kiev at once," cried Volkh, "and ask the little Prince what his wishes are."

"God protect you along the way," said the parish clerk severely—he had not seen the pilgrim and rather doubted the story told him by Martha.

Mother and son turned homewards. She said:

"Volkh, I am afraid it is a far distance for that old pony of yours, and some of the going is rough."

"Oh I wish I had a horse to take me to the very gates of Kiev within an instant," cried the boy, and the very next instant he was in the saddle, a beautiful black horse under him, and he was no longer at the gate of his mother's house. There stood the great turreted walls of Kiev. Beyond, domes, cupolas and roofs blended into a marvelous tapestry of gold, crimson, blue and green. Yet no bells could be heard, and the watch at the gates were sobbing bitterly. Volkh leaped out of the saddle.

"Oh, what has happened?" he asked.

"It is our little Prince Danilo," gulped one of the men. "Yesterday he rode out with his falcon, and he had his bodyguard, too, but he was kidnaped by an enemy from a very far country—they say they are all magicians there, and one of their men shot an arrow into the city with a message for the Prince. I cannot rightly tell you what was in it, but all the Knights of the Golden Table left Kiev within a few minutes. Not one of them has yet returned. Well, young sir, ride on into the city!"

Volkh had heard so much of the crowds, the markets, the gaiety of life in Kiev. He found it a city of mourning. Nobody was to be seen in the streets, and all the shops were closed and the markets empty. The people crowded the Cathedral and all the churches to pray for the rescue of their little Prince, Vladimir's only son and heir. Volkh rode on to the gateway of the palace. He knew well that he had the right to ask to see his sovereign and now he understood why his knightly gear had been given him. Volkh felt very excited and not a little scared. He also remembered that he must be very careful about wishing. He had already expressed one wish for a horse. Five wishes only were left to him.

According to custom Volkh took off his helmet and belt when he reached the porch of the palace. The captain of the men-at-arms asked his name and added:

"Prince Vladimir will not refuse to see you, but have you some really urgent business? He is in great distress."

Volkh replied, his words a surprise to himself:

"I am here to ask for the Prince's blessing. I mean to rescue the little Prince."

The man stared very hard and pulled at his beard.

"Prince Vladimir is in no mood for such unkind jokes, boy. You don't look old enough to carry a sword."

"I am sorry, I had to leave it in the porch together with my helmet and belt. I wish I had it on me to prove—" and Volkh stopped because the belt, the sword dangling from it, was round his waist in an instant.

"Four wishes left," gasped Volkh. "Really, I must be careful."

The captain of the men-at-arms was shaking from head to foot.

"Take it off, take it off at once, and tell it to stay where you put it, and you are not to scare Prince Vladimir the way you scared me."

Presently Volkh was led into the crimson painted hall, and the Prince received him kindly enough.

"Have you come to ask me to right some injustice, son?" he asked.

"No, my lord," Volkh replied. "I have come for your blessing," and he knelt, the tips of his fingers touching the edge of the Golden Table. "I mean to ride and rescue the young Prince."

Vladimir stared.

"You have no idea what you are talking about! He has been taken to a country called Persia—they flew away with him. His bodyguard saw it happen. All Persians are great magicians, and the Shah of Persia has asked for a ransom—ten thousand white heifers without a blemish. All the Knights of the Golden Table have ridden away to look for them. I doubt if they will find as many hundred," and Prince Vladimir sat very still. He thought of his wife, Princess Eupraxia, weeping in her room upstairs.

"I have not got a single white heifer to offer, my lord," said Volkh, "but it is my duty to go," and he told Vladimir about the pilgrim's visit, the miraculous gift of equipment and horse, and the little piece of parchment.

"It is my duty to go, my lord," he said again, and Prince Vladimir raised his right hand.

"God bless you, my son, and He alone can protect you. The hazards are far more than you think."

Volkh rose, bowed, and murmured:

"Oh I wish I were in the saddle and at the place where the young Prince is!"

No sooner had he said it than he found himself in a strange mountainous country. He sat in the saddle, facing a cleft between two huge rocks. To the left stretched a valley covered with innumerable white tents. To the right of him, he saw four huge poles so tall that he could hardly see their tops where two crisscross poles were joined together, and from the middle swung an enormous gilt cage, most sumptuously furnished with cushions and coverlets of white velvet and violet silk; and there sat little Prince Danilo dressed in a pink and green striped Persian robe, with a Persian cap on his head. The very sight of

141

those clothes infuriated Volkh. How dared they put them on a prince of Kiev?

The child raised his head, and Volkh saw that he had been crying.

"I am from Kiev, Prince Danilo," said Volkh and jumped out of the saddle. "I have come to take you home."

The little Prince stood up and clung to the bars.

"You mustn't come too near," he cried. "A kindly Persian woman tried to give me some food, and two huge hounds ran from behind a rock as soon as she touched the bars, and they killed her."

Volkh unsheathed his sword.

"I expect I could deal with those hounds, Prince Danilo, but before I get any nearer, please tell me how the cage opens. The bars go all the way round and there doesn't seem to be a lock anywhere."

"They welded the bars together," sobbed the little Prince. "They said my dear father would never get ten thousand white heifers for my ransom and that I would never come out. Oh dear, I am so hungry and thirsty, too!"

"Keep in good heart, Prince Danilo." Volkh rode nearer and stretched his hands towards the bars. At once two enormous hounds, fangs bared, sprang from behind a rock.

"I wish both of you were dead within an instant," cried Volkh, and down they went at once.

"I have just three wishes left," he thought, "that is— three for myself. Wasn't there something about three wishes for Prince Danilo? I must find out," and he said aloud, "Well, one hurdle is behind us, and don't worry— I mean to get you out, but don't you wish you could have some food before the journey home?"

"Food?" echoed the little Prince. "I wish I had a stale crust to chew!"

Volkh watched narrowly, but no stale crust appeared on the white velvet cushions.

"The spell must work differently for the little Prince," he thought. "And I have three wishes of my own left now. One for the cage to open, one for some food, and the third for the speedy return to Kiev. Now then," Volkh took a deep breath and said "I wish the cage would open," and at once all the bars fell apart and the little Prince jumped down, right into Volkh's arms.

"Steady, Prince," said Volkh. "Now you must not ride hungry," and again he spoke the words, and there was a table covered with a white cloth and laden with dishes; fragrant sturgeon soup, mushroom pies, roast fowl, honey bread and milk in a silver jug, and Prince Danilo urged Volkh to share all the good things with him. When they had eaten, Volkh said:

"Now for home," and he was just about to lift the little Prince into the saddle when Danilo said sadly:

"These dreadful outlandish clothes! My father's people would think I had turned Persian! Oh for my little blue coat and my green boots with tassels!"

"Yes," Volkh nodded sympathetically, "I wish I could bring you home in those clothes," and there stood Prince Danilo in his blue coat and white shirt, its collar worked in red cross-stitch, and the high green boots.

"You are a good magician," the child clapped his hands for pleasure, but Volkh's face had gone white. He had spent the last wish.

"I suppose we had better hurry," said the boy, and Volkh lifted him into the saddle.

143

Volkh's heart was beating wildly. If he turned the horse south, he would ride straight into the Persian camp. If he rode north, he might lose his way in the mountains. How far were they from Kiev? He could not tell, but he felt sure it was a fearful distance.

"Has your horse gone lame?" Prince Danilo asked politely, turned his head, and screamed. "Look, they are going to chase us—"

It was true. Volkh spurred the horse and plunged into the rocky pass. He had spent his last wish, but at least he had a wonderful mount to ride, and the black horse flew like an eagle. Soon their pursuers were left far behind, but Volkh's horse was still galloping through the wild rocky country. For all Volkh knew, they were going farther and farther away from Kiev, and he knew the sun was about to set. What could he do? The little paper mentioned three

wishes for Prince Danilo, but the boy had asked for food, and no food had come . . .

He reined in the horse on a narrow rocky shelf, and dismounted. Suddenly he felt so tired that he would have given all he had for an hour's sleep. The little Prince, still in the saddle, looked down and said softly:

"I suppose we are still far away from Kiev. I wish you

were not so tired," and no sooner had the child spoken than Volkh felt his fatigue slipping away. In fact, he thought he would have enough strength to cleave a rock in two. So here lay the key: the little Prince's wishes worked so long as they did not concern himself. And there were only two of them left. Volkh caught his breath.

"Well, we have ridden a good distance, and we cannot be very far away from Kiev—"

And he was about to mount when Danilo bent down and touched his shoulders.

"Oh, I wish you would not look so sad!"

And instantly Volkh was feeling as happy as he had never felt before—just when there was nothing for him to feel happy about. Then he had an idea, and he staked Danilo's last wish on it. If it failed, they were lost, "and we must not fail," thought Volkh stubbornly.

So he leaped into the saddle and said:

"I am sorry, Prince Danilo. I was thinking of my mother. She did not know I would be coming here. She expected me home quite soon—" and, having said it, Volkh prayed with all his might that the little Prince would answer in the right way.

Danilo said nothing for a minute. Then he whispered:

"Yes, I understand. I wish your mother could see you riding through the streets of Kiev!"

At once the grim rocks were gone. They were riding very slowly down the Street of Wisdom, and Volkh's eyes caught Martha's happy proud face as she stood at the edge of the square. They rode on to the sound of bells and deafening cheers. Vladimir and Eupraxia rushed past the guard to greet them.

A little later Volkh and Martha were summoned into

the crimson hall. All the Knights were still away looking for white heifers for the Prince's ransom, but another oaken chair had been added to the others, and a small red-plumed helmet lay on the table in token of a Knight's presence in the palace. Martha burst into tears of joy, but Volkh stammered that he was not fit to be a Knight.

"But that is for your sovereign to say," Vladimir told him and, bending forward, touched the boy's right shoulder.

Chourilo's Little Comb

THE TENTH TALE
Chourilo's Little Comb

An Eastern potentate had sent Prince Vladimir a pair of extremely rare birds as a wedding present when he married Eupraxia. The birds had delicate pink chests and honey-golden wings. Their tails were emerald-green, and on their heads was a brilliant blue mark shaped like a crown. The Prince and his wife valued those birds very much. They were kept in a great gilt cage in the inner courtyard of the palace, but in time they grew so tame that they flew where they pleased. They ate corn out of Vladimir's hands, and their singing put nightingales to shame. Vladimir and Eupraxia were very pleased when the hen hatched her eggs. As years went on, quite twenty of these beautiful birds lived in Kiev.

It so happened that one summer a young fisherman sat with his rod on the bank of a small tributary of the Dnieper. His name was Chourilo. He had never been to Kiev in his life and had not even heard of the Prince's rare birds.

He sat there, hoping for a bite, but no fish would bite that evening. Chourilo felt rather desperate—he had hoped for at least one fish so that his mother could have a good supper that night. He wondered if he had better saunter off to the woods and get hold of a hare when one of the Prince's birds flew overhead, alighted on the bough of an alder, and began cleaning its feathers. So tame it was that Chourilo's presence did not disturb it at all.

Its marvelous colors certainly attracted him. But it was its size that enchanted Chourilo.

"Why, this would be far better than a pike," he thought, dropped the rod, seized his bow, fitted an arrow, took aim and, blood streaking its pale pink breast, the bird fell off the alder bough. Chourilo was extremely pleased with himself.

But when he came home, his mother was aghast at the sight of the dead bird.

"Do you not know that you have killed one of Prince Vladimir's pet birds?" she said. "Your uncle Ivan used to take corn to Kiev and he has often seen them. They used to live in a huge cage but they got so tame that now they are free, and folk say they fly anywhere and they always get back to the Prince's palace in the end. Why, son, your life would be forfeit if anyone found out!"

Chourilo stooped to pick up the dead bird and put it back in the sack.

"No, Mother, I knew nothing of those wonderful birds. Ah well, I suppose I must walk to Kiev and ask the Prince's pardon. I am sorry—I did so want you to have a good supper tonight."

"Chourilo," his mother burst out crying, "has anyone seen you doing it?"

"Not a soul was anywhere near," he replied.

"Well, then, it may be that nobody will ever find out. I shall pluck it with the door bolted and barred, and I'll bury the feathers three feet deep at the back of the kitchen garden."

But Chourilo shook his flaxen head.

"No, Mother, it is not right."

"You want a good supper much more than I do," his

mother broke in, and he grinned.

"Yes, and there is nothing but thin gruel in the house, but how could you and I enjoy a supper I had no business to get? The Prince is known to be just. Well, I had better start on my way. I'll soon be back and I'll try and catch a hare on the way home."

His mother cried bitterly, so sure was she that she would never see Chourilo again. She set his meager supper of porridge and milk before him, and found a clean smock for him. Then she rummaged in a chest and brought out a small comb of yellowish bone.

"A wise woman gave it to me the day you were born, Chourilo. She told me that the comb would protect you from danger, but our life here has been so peaceful. Never did I think that the day would come when I should give you this comb! Now, whenever you face danger, just comb your hair and your beard, and trust to God to deliver you."

"And if I see someone else in danger?" asked Chourilo as he took the little comb.

"The wise woman said it would work the same way," his mother answered. "I am sure your poor father would never have got drowned in the Nieprad if I had thought he needed the comb."

So Chourilo left the same evening, the dead bird in a sack slung over his left shoulder. He tramped all through the night and reached the gates of Kiev by daybreak. Country born and bred, he had never seen a city before, and the sight of all those houses and churches awed him, but the people he met spoke so kindly to him that he took heart. They told him how to get to the Prince's palace.

"And you need not look so anxious," an elderly mer-

chant said to Chourilo. "The Prince may be at Mass when you get there, but he does not refuse to see anyone. You can be certain of a good breakfast, young man."

Chourilo thanked him politely and thought to himself:

"What do I want with a breakfast? It is his pardon I have come for."

The Prince was indeed at Mass. The palace gateway stood wide open, and Chourilo walked in very shyly. He had never imagined such a building could exist in the world —all gilded turrets and carved balconies and porches painted red and green and a bright blue roof over it all. The very size of the forecourt scared him not a little. There seemed enough space for more than one village.

Chourilo was but a peasant in a patched smock and his feet were bare, but the men-at-arms received him kindly, since such was the custom. Nobody asked him what his business was. He was merely told he would have to wait a little, and led to a bench in a corner, and good food was soon brought to him.

But Chourilo could neither eat nor drink, so troubled he felt. Then he raised his head and rapture stole into his eyes. From a small window on his left a girl leaned out, scattering crumbs to the pigeons, and so lovely she was that Chourilo held his breath. A man passing by him, he asked shyly:

"Who is the young girl in a blue veil and a white cloak feeding the pigeons?"

The man glanced at the window and replied:

"Why, it is Princess Irene, our lord's second daughter. She is always about doing kindnesses to everybody. She loves beasts and birds. She can nurse them, too. I have heard of her nursing a lame hare and a wounded thrush."

Chourilo heard. His heart sank. "So beautiful, so kind, but a princess . . ." Yet he went on looking toward that window. Soon enough his heart was all on fire, and then the girl left the window, and Chourilo wondered if town life were so odd that the sun set at morning: so dark and grey did the forecourt become when the Princess moved away from her window.

Presently, a few of the Knights of the Golden Table began crossing the forecourt on their way to breakfast with the Prince. Chourilo looked at them, dull envy in his heart. Those gallant men, who, as he had heard, stood closest to Vladimir, must often have received their stirrup-cups from those delicate white hands which had fed the pigeons and which knew how to nurse lame hares and wounded thrushes. Chourilo felt he would have given everything in the world for yet another distant glimpse of the girl. But she did not come to the window again.

A little later they led Chourilo into the hall. Prince Vladimir, his breakfast finished, looked up and asked kindly:

"Are you here to complain of an injustice?"

"Lord," Chourilo replied, "nobody has been unjust or unkind to me in my life. I am here to ask your pardon. I am truly sorry for what I have done—all unwittingly—" and he undid the sack and laid the dead bird on the green marble floor. Everybody gasped, and Vladimir's face darkened.

"Did you then dare to set a trap for it, or what?"

"I did not, lord." Chourilo drew a difficult breath and told the Prince how he had come to shoot the bird.

For a moment or two there was silence. Then Vladimir looked at Chourilo keenly and asked:

"And your mother warned you against coming to Kiev?"

"Only because she was troubled about me, lord," replied Chourilo in such a voice that the Prince knew he could not doubt the young man's sincerity.

"And yet you have come here—"

"It would have been a worse dishonor to hide my trespass," said Chourilo.

"Here, then, is my judgment," said Vladimir loudly, and all those present at once rose to their feet to hear the sentence. No one's eyes were on Chourilo, and he stood, head bent, his conscience at ease, his heart aching.

"Here is my judgment," said the Prince again. "There is to be no penalty for the trespass so freely and bravely admitted. Now what reward will you have for your honesty?"

"Lord," Chourilo replied in a voice which did not quite belong to him, "I deserve no reward—"

"That," the Prince smiled, "is for me to say."

And Chourilo took heart.

"I have deserved no reward, lord, but since it is your wish that I should name one, have I your leave to woo Princess Irene?"

Vladimir's face darkened at once.

"You would have had a suitable reward for your honesty. For your temerity I exile you from my dominions for two years, two months and two days. Is that clear? When your exile is finished, come back to Kiev and see me again."

In those days it was law in Kiev that if anyone sentenced to exile had no means of his own, he was given some clothing and a little money to enable him to make a start in a strange country. So it was done in Chourilo's case, and the Prince's almoner told him that his mother would be cared for by the nuns of an abbey at the gates of Kiev.

Chourilo would not have been downhearted if it were

not for his anxiety that Princess Irene might be given in marriage to some prince or noble before he, Chourilo, was back in Kiev. He had seen her just once. He had not exchanged a word with her, and he had no idea whether she would ever listen to him. None the less, he was determined to win her once his exile was ended.

A good fisherman and possessing remarkable skill with his bow and arrows, Chourilo found little difficulty in making his way farther and farther down south from Kiev. People liked his open face and pleasant manner, and were always struck by his honesty. So little by little, he made his way to Constantinople, and the harbor master took him on as an apprentice pilot. It proved a hard enough life and the wage was poor, but Chourilo did not shrink from hardihoods. Months succeeded months, and the thought of Princess Irene never left him. Many travelers from Kiev came to Constantinople. Chourilo often met some of them, and he had just one question to ask: "Has Princess Irene got married?" and the negative answer filled him with joy.

Now it wanted less than two months for his exile to end. Pilot apprenticeship lasted three whole years, and Chourilo could not be said to have distinguished himself in any way —except by hard work and great honesty, but neither of those would have paved the way to any high position in Byzantium. He had left Kiev a poor peasant. It did not seem likely that he would return with gold coins in his pouch and diamond buckles on his shoes.

One evening the master pilot summoned him to go aboard a Sicilian merchantman bound for a port on the Black Sea. The wind was freshening, and the master pilot said grimly that he and Chourilo would be lucky if they got back to harbor in their own cockleshell of a boat.

Hardly had he spoken when a violent storm broke out, and the skipper begged the pilot to turn the ship back to harbor, but such a manoeuvre seemed well-nigh impossible. It looked as though the waters of the Bosphorus were possessed of an evil spirit determined to send every ship down to the bottom. Chourilo was frightened. Now he stood in real peril, but so scared was he that he forgot all about the virtue of the yellow comb. He had never parted with it, nor had he ever had the necessity to use it.

At that moment, away to starboard, they saw a great barge in difficulties. Wild seas were sweeping all over her, and it looked as though her keel would be up-ended any moment, and Chourilo pointed her out to the master pilot who shouted in his ear:

"We are in trouble ourselves and we cannot offer help."

The barge overturned, and Chourilo could see the figure of a woman clinging to the gunwale. Then he remembered the comb. He pulled it out, passed it through his hair and his beard, and leaped into the madly swirling waters.

"Ah well," shouted the master pilot to the skipper, "the lad might have made a fair enough pilot in the end!"

Chourilo swam through those vicious seas as though they were so many ripples across a duckpond. He thrust out his left arm and had the woman safe. He swam back to his own ship, the burden never hampering him. Sailors, speechless at such reckless bravery, helped him hoist the woman aboard, and the storm died down as suddenly as it had come, but the skipper insisted that they should make course for the harbor.

Everybody called Chourilo the hero of heroes, and some men on board even wondered if he were not some great and noble knight doing an apprentice's work as a penance. It was useless for Chourilo to keep on telling them that he was just a very poor peasant from Kiev. The excitement reached its peak when the rescued woman recovered consciousness and they learned her identity: she was Anna, niece of the Emperor of Byzantium. She was young and strikingly beautiful, and it was whispered on all sides that her uncle would make her marry Chourilo. He heard and he did not smile.

When the news reached Constantinople, the people went mad with joy, and poor Chourilo did not know what to do. They put him into a gilded chariot drawn by eight black horses and carried him off to the palace when the purple-gowned Emperor learned from the harbor master that Chourilo was the finest fellow in the world and from the chief pilot that he was a prodigy. Poor Chourilo was thrown into such confusion that on being asked what he would like for dinner, he said that a good fishing-net might do for him. Presently the Emperor asked if he would like to remain in Byzantium, marry his niece, and become the Lord High Admiral of the Greek Navy.

Chourilo did not hesitate:

"Lord, I may not marry your niece. My heart is already engaged in Kiev. As to my becoming Lord High Admiral of your navy, why, I could hardly tell a man-of-war from a herring-boat—for all I have tried to become a pilot. As to remaining in Byzantium, my service is pledged to the Prince of Kiev, and him alone could I serve."

And, as happened so often before, Chourilo was commended for his honesty.

Two years, two months and two days before, he had gone down the Dnieper, a poor and unknown exile. Now he went up the Dnieper in a golden Byzantine barge. Instead of a peasant's rough smock, he wore a purple mantle and many jewels given him by the Emperor. There was music on board, and more than half of the deck space was taken up with chests, bales and bundles crammed with imperial presents—gold and silver goblets and dishes, jewels, sumptuous brocades and rare wines. But Chourilo's thoughts were not engaged with his incredible high fortune. It was some time since he had had any news from home, and he was haunted by the idea that either Princess Irene was already betrothed or that she would not have him.

When they reached Kiev, Chourilo was in such haste to reach Vladimir's palace that he never noticed the sadness which hung over the city. But in the gateway the captain of the men-at-arms looked at Chourilo's purple mantle and said he was very sorry but the Prince could not give audiences to ambassadors. Princess Irene was very ill. A few days before she and her ladies had gone to a meadow to gather mushrooms and a sudden storm had broken out. As they were running back to the palace, the Princess saw a half-naked beggar woman sheltering under a tree. The captain went on sadly:

"The Princess wrapped the woman in her own cloak and forbade her ladies to take off theirs. She got so drenched that a fever set in that evening. Since then we have had the Bishop and his monks bringing various relics, and ten physicians have tried to do all they could, but the Princess has not recognized anyone these two days past," and the man added with a deep sigh: "I hear that she is worn to a shadow and that the illness has destroyed all her beauty, but, sir, she is not loved for her beauty alone. It will be a terrible day for Kiev and the whole of Rus when her saintly heart ceases to beat."

When Chourilo heard, he sat down on the ground, wept, and wished that the waters of the Bosphorus had indeed swallowed him up.

At that moment Prince Vladimir came back from church. He saw a man in a rich purple mantle and he asked the captain of the men-at-arms:

"Who is this great noble? He must be a foreigner. No man in Kiev has such a rich emerald chain. What trouble is he in?"

At these words Chourilo struggled to his feet and said in as steady a voice as he could muster:

"My lord, I am no nobleman and no foreigner, I am but a poor peasant whom you sent into exile two years, two months and two days ago. I have come back, fortune having been more than kind to me. Lord, my trouble is your own. I have heard of Princess Irene's terrible illness. Now I ask your leave to win her hand."

"My daughter," Vladimir replied sadly, "is so ill that she cannot recognize even her own mother. We are in despair. How could anyone win her hand—whatever his fortune be—"

"Let me see her but once," pleaded Chourilo, tears falling down his cheeks, "and I would ask for nothing else."

"I remember you now," said Vladimir, "I pardoned your trespass because of your honesty and I exiled you because you had the temerity to ask for her hand—and I said you were to come back to Kiev when your exile ended. Surely, you never even spoke to my daughter? Did your heart not burn for any girl you may have met on your travels?"

"My heart was on fire for her alone," Chourilo answered proudly. "I carry letters from the Emperor of Byzantium to you, my lord. They will prove to you that I might have had him for my uncle if it were not for Princess Irene—" and he bowed and handed the sealed parchment to the Prince.

Vladimir broke the seal and read all about Chourilo's courage and matchless honesty, and his eyes were full of tears.

"If she were but well, if she were but well—" he murmured almost under his breath, "I would be proud indeed to have you as my son. But she is in such peril that she will never marry either prince or pauper. But come with me and you shall see for yourself," and the Prince led the way up the wide stairs and brought Chourilo into the room where Princess Irene lay unconscious.

The young man hardly dared to draw a breath as he saw her. Of her great beauty there was not a sign. Her cheeks were sunken, her color gone, her mouth had lost its youth, her hair its glossiness. Her clouded eyes were wide open, but she saw nothing. As Chourilo stood at the foot of that carved bed, he knew that he would love her always—even as she was, worn out by illness. He brought out the little yellow comb, and the Princess's ladies whispered in horror:

"How dare you comb your hair in this room?"

But Chourilo took no notice of them. The little comb hidden again, he watched closely until he saw a tremor, a flicker of consciousness in her eyes, and heard her voice:

"I am tired. I am thirsty . . . I am so thirsty . . ." and within a few minutes Princess Irene sat up in bed, looked about her, smiled, and asked one of her ladies if her toothache were any better.

Then Chourilo drew near, knelt by her bed, took off his emerald chain and put it between the Princess's hands.

"My star, my star," he murmured.

Later they all said it was most fitting that one of Prince Vladimir's wedding presents to his daughter was a pair of beautiful pink-breasted birds. That he should have made Chourilo a Knight of the Golden Table went without saying.

Samson and the Doll in Green and Brown

Samson and the Doll in Green and Brown

It happened that a great disaster fell upon Kiev: a fleet of barges bound for Constantinople and laden with a cargo of precious furs was attacked and plundered by pirates. It happened at night when the moon was full. According to the few survivors, the pirates came in small shallow boats and were all masked. Yet one of the Kievans, engaged in a hand-to-hand struggle with a marauder, succeeded in pulling off his mask. The pirate was a Tartar.

Vladimir at once issued orders to skippers and merchants that great secrecy was to be observed about the sailing of barge fleets and the nature of the cargoes they carried. The order was obeyed, and picked watchmen were sent to all the wharves. They could not report a single suspicious detail. The next fleet to sail was laden with corn and sturgeon. It also carried a great quantity of amber. The crews were issued pikes and axes. But, in spite of all the precautions, the barges were attacked and plundered. All the merchants were killed to a man, and out of all the crews there remained but one survivor. His story was so incoherent that nobody could make much sense of it. Yet it seemed obvious that the pirates were Tartars.

All the merchants in Kiev were horrified. They at once went to Prince Vladimir, who was greatly perplexed. Clearly, it seemed a task for the Knights to shoulder, but the Prince did not see how he could send the entire Fellowship to patrol the whole length of the Dnieper. He knew, too, that he could not leave his merchants at the mercy of those pirates.

So he summoned his Knights to a council. According to custom, the first to speak was the youngest among the Knights, a curly-headed giant called Samson, who had won his spur after a fearful battle when his axe had accounted for fifty enemy heads. They all liked Samson for his courtesy and modesty, and they knew him to be no fool.

He got up at a signal from the Prince, and they at once noticed that he looked ill at ease.

"My lord," Samson began, "the Fellowship cannot patrol the whole length of the Dnieper, nor should it be necessary. The root of the trouble is at home. Those pirates get their information from someone within the principality."

The Knights frowned. Ilya of Murom muttered that nothing except nonsense could be expected from a milksop. Dobryna and Chourilo looked angrily contemptuous, and Aliosha laughed. The Prince struck the table with his fist.

"There could be no spies in my dominions," he said fiercily. "Samson, you do not know what you are saying."

The young Knight blushed a deep scarlet.

"I do, my lord. It has happened twice and it will happen again—in spite of all the secrecy. No Tartar lives in the principality, therefore the information must be given by a subject of yours—"

Samson stopped. They all waited. At last Vladimir prompted him:

"Indeed, and who might he be?"

Samson replied calmly:

"From what I have heard, I think it is Spess."

The Knights leaned back and sighed with relief. They hated Spess so much that they were prepared to believe the worst of him.

Spess, a cripple from birth, was a landowner, and he lived on his manor a little to the east of Kiev. He was so fat that a house had to be built specially for him, so greedy that he had twelve courses for dinner and fourteen for supper, so mean that he would have sold the very cobwebs off a ceiling. But the Knights did not loathe Spess for his gluttony or his parsimony. They could not forget the day when Spess was driven into the city and made the men turn his chariot back when he was half-way down the Street of Wisdom, saying that the city was much too muddy for his horses' hooves and that anyhow he knew the food at the Prince's table was hardly fit for pigs. Vladimir had merely laughed. But the Knights had then sworn to avenge the honor of Kiev. No such chance had so far come their way: Spess stayed on at his manor.

Now they listened eagerly.

"Spess?" Vladimir echoed. "Come, Samson, the man has the manners of a pig, but that does not necessarily turn him into a spy. Have you seen any of his men down by the river bank?"

"Never a one, my lord."

"Well, then, what reason can you give us?"

Samson clenched his fists hard.

"My lord, about a week before that first fleet sailed, I happened to meet Klim down by the river bank."

"Ah," said Vladimir, "you were fortunate, Samson! I do wish that fever had not carried Klim away two days ago. He was indeed a soothsayer who never failed me."

"And he is not going to fail you now, my lord. He told me he had been going about the wharves for some time. He mentioned having seen a doll—"

"A what?" they all asked chorally.

"A doll," Samson repeated. "At least, Klim said it was the size of a doll. It wore a brown kirtle and a dark-green shawl, and it went hopping from barge to barge. Klim asked one or two among the skippers about it, but they had not seen it. Klim then tried to get hold of it, and it flew away—"

"It did what?"

"It flew away, my lord. Klim saw a pair of tiny wings under the dark-green shawl. Klim would have come and told you, my lord, but he was taken ill the same day."

Aliosha broke in:

"Come, Samson, the very last witch died when I leveled the Bald Mountain down."

Ilya of Murom said thickly:

"Klim must have had too much mead, my son, and so had you—to believe such a story. A witch is a witch, and a dragon is a dragon—but dolls belong to nurseries."

Vladimir motioned to them to be silent and turned to Samson:

"I never doubted anything my good Klim told me, but what has that doll to do with Spess and the attack on the barges?"

"I cannot answer the last part of your question, my lord, but last evening I happened to ride past Spess's manor. On a window-sill sat a most extraordinary little creature—just as Klim had described it—about the size of a doll, in a brown kirtle and a dark-green shawl. It held a bag and it was counting coins, my lord. My sight is keen.

Those were Tartar coins."

Silence fell among them until the Prince asked:

"What did you do then?"

"I crossed myself twice and rode past hurriedly," answered Samson simply.

One of the Knights remarked:

"Come to think of it, my lord, I now remember my father saying that Spess got his wealth by the practice of dark arts. His parents could not always afford salt for their porridge. It used to be said that a warlock had helped Spess to dig for hidden treasure. Indeed, how else could he have had the money to buy so much land and to live in the way he does?"

Vladimir's right hand pulled at his beard. His blue eyes looked somber. He said:

"Samson, you will ride to Spess's manor today and bring him to Kiev. I could never condemn him unheard. Whatever he has done, he must have a fair trial."

"He will say that our roads are too dirty for his beautiful chariot," Dobryna grumbled, but the Prince silenced him:

"He will never dare to disobey my summons."

That very day Samson rode out of Kiev. He did not feel particularly happy. It was one thing to fight dragons and Tartars. It was a different matter to go and challenge a man, a cripple from birth, who had a magical doll among his possessions. Samson rode, fingering the great silver cross under his hauberk, and he said more prayers in an hour than he had done in a year.

Spess's manor fronted the road and a big wood of silver birches stretched behind it. The house had prettily carved window frames, and the pillared porch was painted bright scarlet. Samson jumped off his horse and gave the bridle to a servant.

"I come from the Prince and I must see your master at once."

The man's face went pale.

"Sir, the master is at dinner. I dare not disturb him. The stuffed pike has only just been carried in. That is the seventh course, and the master has twelve for dinner."

"Did you not hear me say that I come from our sovereign lord?" asked Samson and his voice rang like iron on stone.

The man began trembling like an aspen leaf.

"Sir, I dare not bring you in. The master hardly ever has visitors in the house. The few who do come are received in the porch, but not during meal-times, sir."

Samson had had more than enough. He leaped up the six steps leading to the porch, passed a dim anteroom, pushed open a heavy door, and found himself in a great hall sumptuously furnished with rare hangings and chairs covered with green brocade. All the windows were flung open, but it struck Samson that the air in the hall was very close, and he cast a glance about, but the doll in brown and green was not to be seen anywhere. At a table at the end, Spess, wearing a loose gown of blue velvet sat eating his stuffed pike. By his chair stood a stool with a malachite coffer on it.

On hearing the door open Spess raised his huge head, swallowed, and shouted in a deep voice:

"Who is fool enough to disturb me at dinner?"

"I am a Knight of the Golden Table and I come from the Prince," answered Samson. "Finish your pike, Spess, and tell them to get your chariot ready. You are coming to Kiev with me."

For an answer Spess cut a large slice of the fish and stuffed it into his mouth. As he chewed, he stared at the dish.

"Those are the Prince's orders," Samson went on. "Tell your men to get your chariot ready, Spess. I have said it twice, and I am not going to say it for the third time."

Spess stopped chewing and snarled:

"And what does the Prince want of me? To send men from my manor to clean up the streets of Kiev, I suppose? And high time it was done, too! But my men are not going to do it, nor do I wish to be treated to a stew of rotten herrings."

In an instant Samson ran up to the table, his left hand clutching his sword. Spess laughed.

"Is that the way you are taught to keep your knightly oath?" he mocked. "I am unarmed and I am a cripple. Kill me if you like," here Spess laid his hand on the malachite coffer beside him, "but don't forget that you are alone and I have three hundred and eight men on the manor."

Spess did not exaggerate: he had three hundred and eight men on the manor, but they were all cowards. They could not have fought a spider on the wall. As soon as they had heard from the groom about an armed Knight's arrival, they had all run away into the wood.

"I would not touch you," Samson cried, "and I have had no orders to kill you. I could fight a knight or an honest enemy, and you are neither."

"I am a cripple and I am unarmed," Spess repeated softly, "but I have a weapon of which you know nothing, young man. The Prince thinks I am in league with the pirates, and so I am, so I am," Spess rubbed his huge red hands together. "What does Kiev mean to me? Less than nothing, and my alliance with the pirates is as profitable as I choose to make it."

"So I guessed right," Samson flung at him. "You are a traitor!"

"Such a very silly word," Spess said throatily. "I suppose you think me a fool for having admitted my friendship with the Tartars, but you will never leave the manor, young man. I dislike people who pry into my secrets," and Spess raised the lid of the malachite coffer.

Samson all but staggered back. The hideous doll in a brown kirtle and a dark-green shawl lay there. Seen so closely, she looked more dreadful than ever. Her tiny yellow-green eyes were open, and she gave Samson a look of utter venom.

"That is my weapon," laughed Spess, "and not one of your sorcerers can meddle with her. That stupid Klim thought he would catch her, but Polia contrived to kill him by sending him a fatal fever. She has got wings under her shawl, and she gets to the pirates' camp in less time than it takes me to eat a herring's tail. She is so intelligent, too. She never makes a mistake about the time the barges sail or about their cargoes. Since you are going to die so soon, I don't mind admitting that there are certain things Polia cannot do—the warlock who made her for me died before he had quite finished with her, but what she can do is good enough for me," and Spess guffawed. "Well, young man, what have you got to say before I decide in which way you are going to die?"

"Give me time to think while you are finishing your dinner," Samson answered, "and please close the lid to the coffer."

"Ah, you have taken a dislike to my poor Polia." Spess

shook his head but he closed the malachite coffer, and
Samson felt as though a cloud had gone off his mind. Al-
though it still felt close in the hall, yet it seemed easier to
breathe once the coffer was lidded.

He made for the nearest chair and was lost in deep
thought. Meanwhile the servant brought a boar's head, a
big joint of pork, a pigeon pie, an enormous apple pie and
a bowl of stewed cherries. Spess remarked just before he
finished the boar's head:

"I would have offered you some dinner, young man,

but I did not know you were coming, and there is just enough for me. Besides, why should I be expected to feed a man who will be dead in an hour?"

Samson did not answer. His thoughts were absorbed in a remark made by Spess that there were some things that dreadful doll could not do. What were they? Samson thought and thought, and then decided to plunge at random. He remembered that there was no measure to Spess's greed and vanity.

"With a weapon like yours," he said carelessly, "I wonder you should go to the trouble of making friends with pirates. I think they would not be above cheating you of your share in the plunder."

Spess shrugged and attacked the joint of pork.

"Perhaps so, but they have not done it so far. And my little Polia is marvelous. Why, she can carry twelve hundred silver coins on her back."

"Still I rather marvel at you," Samson persisted. "You could get fabulously rich without entangling yourself in any piratical ventures. Why, there is Kiev—almost at your door. You love jewels, Spess, don't you? Just think what your doll could bring you after one single visit to St. So-phia's Cathedral! To mention but one thing out of many, there is the shrine of Our Lady of Sudden Joy—its pearls and rubies alone are worth more than ten princes' ransom."

"No," said Spess in an oddly tautened voice, "I would never send my Polia there."

"Why not? As you say, I am about to die and nobody would know, and it is as easy as picking raspberries—there are no guards in the Cathedral."

"I'd rather not," Spess repeated. He stopped eating, and

176

added, "Polia would never do it. She prefers dealing with Tartar pirates. I am sure she would not like it."

"Well, why not ask her?" Samson urged, drops of sweat beading his forehead. He had staked everything. Would he win? Would he lose? And would he have the time to do what he had in mind?

Rather reluctantly Spess raised the lid of the malachite coffer. At a sign from him the hideous doll got up, scrambled out of the coffer and slid down on the floor, a grin on her painted face. Once again the hall became dreadfully airless, and Samson's heart hammered. Would Spess put the question, or would he order the creature to destroy him immediately? Samson hoped that the idea of pearls and rubies worth more than ten princes' ransom had attracted Spess, who said in a soft ingratiating voice:

"Polia, my dear, you know how much I like silver and gold, but I like pearls and rubies even better."

At once Samson pulled his great silver cross from under the hauberk, slipped off the chain, and held the cross in front of the doll. In less than an instant the painted face darkened and wrinkled up, and a groan rang in the room. Spess screamed at Samson:

"Put it away . . . Put it away . . . You are killing her . . . You are killing her . . ."

And he stretched out his arms, but he could reach neither Samson nor the creature on the floor. Now the doll's face was shriveled to the size of a small nut, the shoulders sagged and sagged until at last, the head thrown back, the doll collapsed. The next moment there was nothing to see except a few pieces of brown silk and dark-green cloth, and Samson stamped on them with his heavily booted foot.

"Well, Spess, that was the only answer she could give, was it not, the Devil's daughter that she was? Little wonder you did not dare to send her to the churches in Kiev."

No answer came. Samson looked up. In his great chair, his head lolling on one side, Spess was dead.

"Hardly an adventure for a Knight," thought Samson as he made for the door. His horse awaited him. The man was nowhere to be seen. Out in the open, under God's clean skies, Samson stopped briefly and realized that the peril he had faced was not to be compared in horror with the danger of any battle. He took off his helmet, crossed himself twice, wiped his forehead, and rode back to Kiev.

Ilya of Murom looked sceptical on hearing about it, but Samson's story bore its proof soon enough: no other attack was ever made again on merchant barges bound for Byzantium.

Nikita and the Last of the Dragons

Nikita and the Last of the Dragons

MANY years had gone and the Knights of the Golden Table had won so many victories that, apart from the occasional threat of the Tartars, things were tranquil enough in Kiev. The Bald Mountain was no more; roads and waterways were clear of dragons, brigands and witches, and Prince Vladimir's neighbors had heard so much about the valor of the Knights that they would not have dreamed of invading the Principality. The Prince and his wife, Eupraxia, said to each other that it looked as though a golden age had indeed come to Kiev.

And then suddenly that peace was broken by a flying dragon, Tougarin.

It was on a March morning that he invaded Vladimir's dominions, and by May the people were in utter despair. There seemed to be no protection against the monster's fearful depredations. Tougarin flew so high in the air that no arrows could reach him. He was nearly twenty-five feet from head to tail. He moved like lightning, and not even Ilya's famous cudgel could catch him. One by one, the Knights tried to work all their magical weapons on him, but Tougarin always escaped right into the clouds— Aliosha's music and Chourilo's little yellow comb were equally useless.

Tougarin's appearance struck terror; his skin was dazzling green with several gold-brown spots, there were horns on his head, and his eyes were like gigantic saucers.

His wings were like those of a bat in shape, but so pale and thin were they that it was possible to see daylight through them. He came down quietly enough, but he rose up with a terrifying roar. It produced a sound like the hissing of one thousand angry snakes.

Tougarin appeared everywhere, and he killed and ravaged without mercy. He would swoop down on a market stall, scatter the panic-stricken people, kill a few of them, and then rise up in the air again, a whole side of beef or a bolt of some expensive fabric in his huge jaws. He stole cows, horses and sheep from the fields. He killed fishermen as they sat mending their nets and hunters when they

were stalking a bear. Not even the cunning of Aliosha or Dobryna could even track Tougarin to his lair. It really looked as though he had made his home in the clouds.

Tougarin spoke in a human language, and the people of Kiev learned his name from himself. On occasions, perched very high up, he would indulge in singing. He sang most offensive songs about Kiev so that people said he must have learned them from Spess. But Tougarin did not stop at mocking Vladimir's food and finding fault with the streets of Kiev. He prophesied that all sorts of disasters would fall on the city. He sang most biting satires about the clothes worn by the Kievans, their customs, and their language. There was one particular song in which Tougarin threatened them with drought and famine for ten years to come. In yet another piece of doggerel he told the people that the waters of the Dnieper would be poisoned on the day when he, Tougarin, decided he had had enough of Kiev.

Gloom fell on Vladimir's dominions. Many murmurs were heard against the Knights of the Golden Table, none among whom seemed strong enough to best Tougarin and to put an end to his depredations. People kept their windows shuttered by day and by night, and mothers were terrified of letting their children go out of doors. Vladimir begged his Princess to say her prayers in the palace chapel and never to venture away from the palace. Fewer and fewer foreign merchants came to the city, and peasants dared not come with their appointed tribute of corn, root vegetables, honey, and fish.

July brought torrential rains to Kiev, and Tougarin vanished. But the respite did not last. As soon as fair weather set in again, the monster's dreadful hissing was heard in the air. In one day alone Tougarin killed five men of Vladimir's bodyguard, wrought fearful damage at the market place, and flew away, a Knight's horse between his horrible jaws.

Now the youngest Knight at the time was one Nikita, a blacksmith's son, very brave in battle and a good companion at table. One wet September morning Nikita went to mass at the Cathedral, and he stood a little to the left of Prince Vladimir, who noticed that his youngest Knight was praying with very great fervor. When the service was over, Vladimir said to Nikita:

"I suppose you were praying for our speedy deliverance from that dreadful dragon?"

But Nikita blushed and replied:

"No, my lord. I prayed for my own enlightenment."

The Prince did not quite like such an answer, but it was raining very hard, and he hurried back to the palace. That same day, however, Nikita came to see him after dinner. The Prince happened to be busy with his treasurer in a small room at the back of the hall, and Nikita had to wait for quite a time. Aliosha passed and suggested that they might have a game of darts that evening, but Nikita stammered that he did not know whether he would be free. So white and troubled he looked that Aliosha wondered not a little but he asked no questions.

When the treasurer had left, Vladimir sent for Nikita.

"My lord," said the young man, his eyes on the ground, "I believe I can see a way to get rid of Tougarin for good."

Vladimir's eyes went very stern.

"Nikita, I did not like what you said to me this morning. I like your last words even less. Ilya of Murom failed to destroy the monster, and so did Dobryna and other Knights—all of them senior to you. You have great valor but hardly any experience, and I will not have braggarts in the Fellowship."

"My lord," Nikita said very humbly, "you are right to say so, but I am no braggart. I took it all to God's altar this morning. Did we not have a respite from Tougarin's depredations all through July?"

"Of course we did," the Prince replied a little testily.

"And you will remember, my lord, that there was not a single fine day that month?"

"Well, yes, that is so."

"Has anyone seen or heard the dragon today?" went

on Nikita, and Vladimir shook his head.

"No, and I heard that everybody has been very busy at the market today."

"And it has been raining hard since before daybreak. My lord, Tougarin dare not come in wet weather; his wings would not carry him. They are made of thin transparent paper."

"I see," the Prince said slowly, "but this discovery does not really help us much. Tougarin avoids wet weather. On fine days it is impossible to catch him."

Nikita said boldly:

"My lord, I suggest that we make it wet for him on a fine day," and, without losing a moment, he laid his plan before the Prince.

Vladimir listened, his eyes grave. Then he picked up a quill and twisted it in his fingers.

"Well, I believe that even if you were to perish, you would not have failed, Nikita. It is a brave idea, and all the people in Kiev will bless you forever."

Wet weather held for about a week, and all the preparations could be carried out without any interference from Tougarin.

There was a very high tower in Kiev, known as Igor's Keep. At the Prince's orders, hundreds and hundreds of big tubs filled with water were carried to the very top. About six or seven feet below, a wide ledge ran all round the keep, and to that ledge the palace kitchen staff brought several enormous roast joints, geese, fowls and meat pies until the ledge began looking like a gigantic market stall. As soon as that was done, Nikita, armed with an axe and a pike, climbed to the very top and stayed there among the water tubs.

The weather changed. The very first bright morning brought Tougarin back to Kiev. The sight of the good things spread on the ledge of Igor's Keep at once attracted the monster. He flew right over the tower but he could not see Nikita, so well hidden was the young Knight among the water tubs. Tougarin gobbled up a leg of pork in an instant, and evidently decided to stay and have a good breakfast while he was about it.

Meanwhile the Prince, all the Knights, and a small crowd had gathered below. They saw Nikita's unhelmeted head at the very edge of the top just when Tougarin was swallowing an enormous meat pie which would have been enough dinner for six. At that very moment a huge tub of water came pouring down, but Tougarin turned and the deluge fell all over his tail. It so enraged him that thick smoke came out of his nostrils, and the people gasped in horror.

"Surely, this will be the end of the poor gallant Knight!"

But, lightning-quick, Nikita seized another tub, and this time the water went all over the monster's head. With a deafening hiss, Tougarin began shaking his head to get the water out of his eyes, and the people saw him just about to spread his huge wings when Nikita sprang, a tub in each arm, and every drop of the water fell across the great pale wings. At once they crumpled up, and with another roar Tougarin fell to the ground, where Ilya's cudgel killed him in an instant.

They cheered Nikita all the way to the palace. Women ran after him, throwing flowers down at his feet, and even little children clapped their hands. There was a solemn service of thanksgiving at the Cathedral, and Prince Vladimir ordered a feast for everybody. At dinner in the hall of the palace, the Prince had Nikita seated in the great red-canopied chair, and Princess Eupraxia's own hands hung a diamond chain round the young Knight's neck. They feasted, sang and danced till sunrise, and for the first time in many months the people of Kiev were not afraid to come out and stroll in the streets with the sun shining upon them.

Tougarin proved the last of the dragons. None other ever came to molest the city of Vladimir, and the Fellowship kept it safe from the threat of the Tartar.

But within five years Vladimir died and then peace walked away from Kiev for a long time. There were princes who quarreled, and princes who had small concern for their people, and princes who had little idea of honor, broke their promises, and betrayed their friends. Fewer and fewer young men offered themselves for the Fellowship, and those who were its members often felt as though their hearts would break—so much injustice and cruelty did they see at Kiev. They no longer feasted at the Golden Table—there was no Golden Table at the palace. They were no longer called to give their counsel to the Prince—he did not need it. They no longer rode nearest their lord in battle—he preferred to have hired warriors close to him.

The time came when there were just twelve Knights of Vladimir's company left, and the oldest among them was Volkh, whose long beard was now pure silver. He called his comrades together and told them it was time they left Kiev. They agreed. According to the knightly custom, they spent the last night in the Cathedral, their gleaming shields placed on the steps leading up to the altar. At sunrise they rode out of the gates, and nobody marked their going. The people of Kiev were too full of their troubles and grievances, and the Prince would not have cared greatly if he knew, but he did not know.

The twelve Knights rode out into the plain. They neither sang nor spoke until Volkh reined in his horse and said:

"Our banner of St. Andrew is left behind in Kiev, but look, here are the cornflowers and here is yarrow. God's wild flowers will serve us for silk and linen."

So they all dismounted and gathered great sheaves of cornflowers and armfuls of yarrow. These they wove into garlands for their horses and themselves, white and blue—the colors of St. Andrew's banner.

They rode for three days and three nights. On the fourth morning, at daybreak, they rode up a great hill and turned eastward. At that moment they became like eagles so that they could look at the rising sun—and such was the warmth of its greeting that the soul of every Knight could not resist it, and eastward they rode until the sun accepted them forever.

And thus ended the Fellowship of the Golden Table, but the memory of those men did not perish. Each succeeding generation of the Russians knew of their valor in song and story. And even more than that. For the honest and brave "*bogatyri*," Ilya of Murom, Dobryna, Samson, and others, were seen riding their mounts high in the air during the battle of Kulikovo in 1380 when the strength of the Tartar yoke was weakened for ever. They gave their blessing to the Russian arms in Poland and Prussia, in Sweden and Turkey, in Italy, and on the borders of Austria. Peasants, dressed in soldiers' uniforms, felt their presence and many insisted that they had seen the gallant *Druzhina* of old Prince Vladimir. So legends tell us.

Still, the most ancient legend of all has a haunting quality all its own: twelve true and honest men, cornflowers and yarrow in their hands and on their horses' necks, riding to keep their tryst with the sun, to them ever a symbol of truth.

About the Author

E. M. ALMEDINGEN lives in a charming seventeenth-century cottage in Britain's West Country, where she writes, gardens (tulips are her special forte) and enjoys classical music. Born and privately educated in St. Petersburg (now Leningrad), Russia, she arrived in London in 1923 with sixpence in her pocket and has been supporting herself with her writing ever since. Now a British citizen, Miss Almedingen has been elected Fellow of the Royal Society of Literature, has lectured at Oxford, and is a noted scholar and writer. Many of her books have appeared in the United States: *Young Catherine, Tomorrow Will Come, Catherine the Great, Frossia, Winter in the Heart,* and *Dasha,* to name but a few. Her chief enthusiasm is for medieval history, and to her retelling of the adventures of the Knights of the Golden Table she brings both love and scholarship.

Twelve stories of the Kiev Cycle recounting the valorous deeds of a group of knights similar to those of King Arthur. They put duty first, defend Vladimir's palace and Kiev against every evil—witch, dragon, pirate or Tartar.